Edexcel

GCSE MODULAR MATHEMATICS
Examples and Practice

FOUNDATION

Stage 2

1
2
3
4
5
6
7
8
9

Heinemann

Edexcel
Success through qualifications

About this book

This *Examples and Practice* book is designed to help you get the best possible grade in your Edexcel GCSE maths examination. The authors are senior examiners and coursework moderators and have a good understanding of Edexcel's requirements.

Foundation Stage 2 Examples and Practice covers all the topics that will be tested in your Foundation Stage 2 examination. You can use this book to revise in the run up to your exam, or you can use it throughout the course, alongside the *Edexcel GCSE Maths* Foundation core textbook.

References in the contents list for each section of the book tell you when to find the most relevant paragraph of the specification. For example, NA2a refers to Number and Algebra, paragraph 2, section a.

Helping you prepare for your exam

To help you prepare, each topic offers:
- **Key points** to reinforce the key teaching concepts
- **Teaching references** showing you where the relevant material is covered in both the old and new editions of the *Edexcel GCSE Maths* Foundation core textbook. These references show you where to find full explanations of concepts, and additional worked examples e.g.

> Teaching reference:
> *(pp 47–49, section 3.1, 3.2)* ——— The first reference is to the old edition
> pp 53–56, section 3.2, 3.3 ——— The second reference is to the new edition

Where material is new to the new specification there is no reference to the old edition textbooks.
- **Worked examples** showing you how to tackle a problem and lay out your answer
- **Exercises** with references showing you which exercises in the *Edexcel GCSE Maths* Foundation core textbook contain similar questions. The first reference, in brackets and italic, is to the old edition. The second reference is to the new edition
- **A summary of key points** so you can check that you have covered all the key concepts

Exam practice and using the answers

An exam style practice paper at the back of the book will help you make sure that you are totally exam-ready. This paper is exactly the same length and standard as your actual Stage 2 exam.

Answers to all the questions are provided at the back of the book. Once you have completed an exercise you can use the answers to check whether you have made any mistakes. You need to show full working in your exam – it isn't enough to write down the answer.

Which edition am I using?

The new editions of the *Edexcel GCSE Maths* core textbooks have yellow cover flashes saying "ideal for the 2001 specification". You can also use the old edition (no yellow cover flash) to help you prepare for your Stage 1 exam.

Contents

Heinemann Educational Publishers,
Halley Court, Jordan Hill, Oxford, OX2 8EJ
a division of Reed Educational & Professional Publishing Ltd
Heinemann is a registered trademark of Reed Educational & Professional Publishing Ltd

OXFORD   MELBOURNE   AUCKLAND
JOHANNESBURG   BLANTYRE   GABORONE
IBADAN   PORTSMOUTH NH (USA)   CHICAGO

First published 2002

ISBN 0 435 53543 9

06   05   04   03   02
10   9   8   7   6   5   4   3   2

Designed and typeset by Tech-Set Ltd, Gateshead, Tyne and Wear
Cover photo: Stone Picture Library
Cover design by Miller, Craig and Cocking
Printed in the United Kingdom by Scotprint

Acknowledgements
The publishers and authors would like to thank Jean Linsky for her contribution and assistance with the manuscript.

The answers are not the responsibility of Edexcel.

Publishing team	Design	Production	Author team
Editorial	Phil Richards	David Lawrence	Karen Hughes
Sue Bennett	Colette Jacquelin	Jason Wyatt	Trevor Johnson
Lauren Bourque			Peter Jolly
Des Brady			David Kent
Nicholas Georgiou			Keith Pledger
Derek Huby			
Maggie Rumble			
Nick Sample			
Harry Smith			
Isabel Thomas			

Tel: 01865 888058   www.heinemann.co.uk

1 Powers, indices and calculators

1.1 Squares, cubes and square roots

- A square number is the result of multiplying one number by itself.

- A cube number is the result of multiplying one number by itself, then multiplying by the number again.

- A square root is a number that has been multiplied by itself to make another number.

$7 \times 7 = 49$
7×7 can be written as 7^2 (7 squared).
$7 \times 7 \times 7$ can be written as 7^3 (7 cubed).
$\sqrt{49}$ means the square root of 49.
7 is the positive square root of 49 because 7 is a positive number.

Example 1

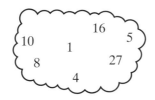

From the numbers in the cloud, write down:
(a) the square numbers
(b) the cube numbers.

(a) 1, 4 and 16 are square numbers because
$1 = 1 \times 1$
$4 = 2 \times 2$
$16 = 4 \times 4$

(b) 1, 8 and 27 are cube numbers because
$1 = 1 \times 1 \times 1$
$8 = 2 \times 2 \times 2$
$27 = 3 \times 3 \times 3$

Example 2

Work out:
(a) 6^2 (b) 2^3 (c) $\sqrt{25}$ (d) the positive square root of 100.

(a) $6^2 = 6 \times 6 = 36$
(b) $2^3 = 2 \times 2 \times 2 = 8$
(c) $\sqrt{25} = 5$ because $5 \times 5 = 25$
(d) the positive square root of $100 = 10$ because $10 \times 10 = 100$.

Exercise 1A   Links (1L) 1M

1   Find the next 4 square numbers after 1, 4, 9, . . .

2   Write down the value of:
   (a) 5 squared   (b) 8 squared
   (c) 11^2 (d) 3^2

  (e) 15^2 **(f)** 21 squared
  (g) 40 squared   **(h)** 100^2.

3 Find the next 3 cube numbers after 1, 8, 27, ...

4 Write down the value of:
  (a) 4 cubed   **(b)** 10^3
  (c) 8 cubed   **(d)** 7 cubed
  (e) 6^3 **(f)** 20^3.

5 Work out:
  (a) $\sqrt{36}$ **(b)** $\sqrt{81}$
  (c) the positive square root of 100
  (d) the positive square root of 25
  (e) $\sqrt{400}$ **(f)** the square root of 625.

6

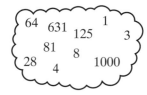

From the numbers in the cloud write down:
  (a) the square numbers   **(b)** the cube numbers.

1.2 Indices and powers

■ The ^{2} in 7^2 is called an *index* or a *power*. It tells you how many
times the given number must be multiplied by itself.

Example 3
Find the value of:
(a) 2^4 (b) 3 to the power 5   (c) $2^2 \times 3^3$.

(a) $2^4 = 2 \times 2 \times 2 \times 2 = 16$
(b) 3 to the power $5 = 3^5 = 3 \times 3 \times 3 \times 3 \times 3 = 243$
(c) $2^2 = 2 \times 2 = 4$, $3^3 = 3 \times 3 \times 3 = 27$
   $2^2 \times 3^3 = 4 \times 27 = 108$

$3 \times 3 \times 3 \times 3 \times 3$ written
in index form is 3^5
because 3 has been
multiplied by itself 5
times.

Exercise 1B   **Links 1N**

1 Find the value of:
  (a) 2^5 **(b)** 4 to the power 4
  (c) 1^6 **(d)** 10 to the power 4
  (e) 5^4 **(f)** 6 to the power 5.

2 Write the following using index notation:
  (a) $2 \times 2 \times 2 \times 2$ **(b)** $4 \times 4 \times 4 \times 4 \times 4$
  (c) $1 \times 1 \times 1 \times 1 \times 1 \times 1$ **(d)** $8 \times 8 \times 8$
  (e) 6×6 **(f)** $7 \times 7 \times 7 \times 7$

3 Complete the table for powers of 10:

Power of 10	Index	Value	Value in words
	3		A thousand
10^2		100	
		1000 000	A million
	1	10	
10^5	5		

4 Work out the value of:

(a) $2^2 \times 5^2$ (b) $4^2 \times 2^3$ (c) $5^2 \times 2^3$ (d) $4^3 \times 10^2$ (e) 4×10^2
(f) 6×10^3 (g) $10^2 \div 5^2$ (h) $10^3 \div 2^3$ (i) $4^3 \div 2^2$

1.3 Using a calculator to solve problems

Teaching reference:
(*pp 311–312, section 24.1*)
pp 371–374, section 24.1

The examples in this section work on Casio calculators. Your teacher will tell you whether you need to change any of the instructions.

Example 4

Work out:

(a) $\dfrac{57 \times 3.4}{25 + 41}$

(b) $3.2^2 \times \sqrt{5 - 3.79}$

(c) $5^5 \times 2^6$

(d) $\dfrac{\sqrt{1.96}}{2.5^3 \times 4}$

(e) $\dfrac{1}{\sqrt{0.04}}$

Remember to use BIDMAS (Brackets, Indices, Divide, Multiply, Add, Subtract) to work out the order of operations.

(a) $\dfrac{57 \times 3.4}{25 + 41} = \dfrac{(57 \times 3.4)}{(25 + 41)}$

Press (5 7 × 3 . 4) ÷ (2 5 + 4 1) =
$= 2.936\,363\,636$

(b) $3.2^2 \times \sqrt{5 - 3.79} = 3.2^2 \times \sqrt{(5 - 3.79)}$

Press 3 . 2 x^2 × √ (5 − 3 . 7 9) =
$= 11.264$

(c) $5^5 \times 2^6$

Press 5 x^y 5 × 2 x^y 6 =
$= 200\,000$

(d) $\dfrac{\sqrt{1.96}}{2.5^3 \times 4} = \dfrac{(\sqrt{1.96})}{(2.5^3 \times 4)}$

Press (√ 1 . 9 6) ÷ (2 . 5 x^y 3 × 4) =
$= 0.0224$

(e) $\dfrac{1}{\sqrt{0.04}}$ Press 1 ÷ √ . 0 4 =
$= 5$

Exercise 1C   Links 24A

1   Work out:

(a) $\dfrac{64}{3+5}$ (b) $\dfrac{4.7-1.1}{2\times 3}$ (c) $\dfrac{16.4 \div 0.2}{41 \times 0.4}$

2   Work out:

(a) 4.7^2 (b) 2.1^3 (c) 5.7^4

(d) 1.2^6 (e) $\sqrt{6.25}$ (f) $\sqrt{5.29}$

3   Work out:

(a) $\sqrt{15.2 - 2.24}$ (b) $\sqrt{3.2 + 3.05}$

(c) $(2.3)^2 \times \sqrt{11.56}$ (d) $4.1^2 \times \sqrt{4.5 - 2.1}$

(e) $\sqrt{2.7 \times 1.5 \times 2.1^2}$

4   Work out:

(a) $\dfrac{2.1^2 \times 3.2^2}{5.2 - 1.1}$ (b) $\dfrac{6.8 - 2.4}{\sqrt{6.1 - 2.1}}$

(c) $\dfrac{5.3 \times 2.7^3}{3.4^2 \times \sqrt{2.5}}$ (d) $\sqrt{\dfrac{5.3 - 2.1}{1.1 + 2.3}}$

5   Work out:

(a) $\dfrac{1}{4(3+2)}$ (b) $\dfrac{1}{\sqrt{25}}$ (c) $\dfrac{1}{0.2 \times 0.4}$ (d) $\dfrac{1}{\sqrt{0.09}}$

Exercise 1D   Mixed questions

1

1	2	3	4	5	6
7	8	9	10	11	12
13	14	15	16	17	18
19	20	21	22	23	24
25	26	27	28	29	30
31	32	33	34	35	36

(a) Copy the above table and put a circle around the square numbers and a cross through the cube numbers.

(b) Which number in the table is both a square number and a cube number?

2   Write down the value of:

(a) 4^2 (b) 8^3 (c) 17 squared   (d) 21 cubed

(e) $\sqrt{8100}$ (f) the positive square root of 3969.

3 Write down the following using index notation:
    (a) $6 \times 6 \times 6$ **(b)** 11×11 **(c)** $2 \times 2 \times 2 \times 2 \times 2 \times 2$

4 Write down the value of:
    (a) 5^4 **(b)** 2^7 **(c)** 10^3 **(d)** 10^5

5 Work out the value of:
    (a) $3^2 \times 4^2$ **(b)** $2^4 \times 7^2$ **(c)** 4×10^2 **(d)** 3×10^4

6 Use your calculator to work out:
    (a) $\dfrac{5.1 \times 2.3}{5.6 - 2.1}$ **(b)** $2.1^2 \times \sqrt{3.1 + 2.2}$ **(c)** $\sqrt{\dfrac{2.4^3 \times 3.1}{2.1 \times 1.4}}$ **(d)** $\dfrac{1}{\sqrt{0.49}}$

Summary of key points

- A square number is the result of multiplying one number by itself.
- A cube number is the result of multiplying one number by itself, then multiplying by the number again.
- A square root is a number that has been multiplied by itself to make another number.
- The ^{2} in 7^2 is called an *index* or a *power*. It tells you how many times the given number must be multiplied by itself.

2 Fractions, percentages, proportion and compound measures

2.1 Writing one number as a fraction of another

Example 1

Mary has 1000 books. Of these books, 648 are fiction. The others are non-fiction.
What fraction of Mary's books are

(a) fiction
(b) non-fiction?

(a) 648 out of 1000 are fiction.

$$\text{The fraction is } \frac{648}{1000}$$

$$\text{so the answer in its simplest form } = \frac{81}{125}$$

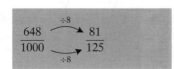

(b) 1000 − 648 = 352 books are non-fiction.

$$\text{The fraction is } \frac{352}{1000} = \frac{44}{125}$$

Exercise 2A   Links (4B) 4B

1   In a class of 30 pupils 16 are girls.
    What fraction of the class are
    (a) girls   (b) boys?

2   40 flowers are grown from a packet of seeds. 15 are blue and
    20 are red. The rest are yellow.
    What fraction of the flowers are
    (a) blue   (b) red   (c) yellow?

3   Fozia earns £360 a week. She spends £30 on travel, £50 on
    food and £120 on household bills.
    What fraction of her earnings does Fozia spend on
    (a) travel   (b) food   (c) bills?
    (d) What fraction of her earnings is left?

4   Graham wins £1000. He saves £400 and spends the rest.
    What fraction of the prize does Graham spend?

5 Pam travels from her home to her friend's home. The total length of the journey is 275 km, including 165 km on a motorway. What fraction of Pam's journey is
(**a**) on a motorway (**b**) not on a motorway?

6 Out of 150 pupils in a year group, 30 walk to school. Write this as a fraction in its simplest form.

7 Five apples in a box of a hundred are rotten. What fraction of the apples are not rotten?

8 Jules is given £5 pocket money. She spends £2.40 on chocolate and £2 on magazines.
What fraction of her pocket money does Jules
(**a**) spend on chocolate,
(**b**) spend on magazines,
(**c**) have left?

2.2 Converting between fractions, percentages and decimals

Teaching reference: pp 230–234, section 14.2

■ **To write a percentage as a fraction, always use the denominator 100.**

■ **To write a percentage as a decimal:**
  ● **write the percentage as a fraction**
  ● **convert the fraction to a decimal**
  ● **or simply divide the percentage by 100.**

■ **To change a decimal to a percentage, multiply the decimal by 100.**

■ **To write a fraction as a percentage:**
  ● **change the fraction to a decimal**
  ● **multiply the decimal by 100.**

Example 2
(a) Write 65% as (i) a fraction
                 (ii) a decimal.
(b) Write $17\frac{1}{2}\%$ as (i) a fraction
                 (ii) a decimal.

(a) (i) $65\% = \dfrac{65}{100} = \dfrac{13}{20}$

  (ii) $65\% = \dfrac{65}{100} = 65 \div 100 = 0.65$

(b) (i) $17\frac{1}{2}\% = \dfrac{17\frac{1}{2}}{100} \overset{\times 2}{\underset{\times 2}{=}} \dfrac{35}{200} = \dfrac{7}{40}$

  (ii) $17\frac{1}{2}\% = \dfrac{35}{200} = 35 \div 200 = 0.175$

Example 3

Change to a percentage:

(a) 0.35   (b) 0.125   (c) $\dfrac{4}{20}$ (d) $\dfrac{18}{80}$

(a) $0.35 \times 100 = 35\%$

(b) $0.125 \times 100 = 12.5\%$

(c) $\dfrac{4}{20} = 4 \div 20 = 0.2$

$0.2 \times 100 = 20$

so $\dfrac{4}{20} = 20\%$

(d) $\dfrac{18}{80} = 18 \div 80 = 0.225$

$0.225 \times 100 = 22.5$

so $\dfrac{18}{80} = 22.5\%$

Example 4

Penny earns £960 a month.
Her rent is 45% of her income and she spends $\frac{1}{5}$ of her income on bills. The remainder is available to spend on what she chooses.

(a) How much does Penny spend on her rent and bills?

(b) Write this as a fraction of her income.

(a) £960 $\times$ 0.45 = £432; $\frac{1}{5}$ = .20 so .20 $\times$ 960 = £192;
£432 + £192 = £624

(b) 65% or 65/100

Exercise 2B   Links (*14A–C*) 14B, 14C

1 Write the following percentages as fractions:
   (a) 20%   (b) 50%   (c) 25%   (d) 75%
   (e) 32%   (f) 64%   (g) $37\frac{1}{2}\%$ (h) $62\frac{1}{2}\%$

2 Write the following percentages as decimals:
   (a) 30%   (b) 70%   (c) 45%   (d) 85%
   (e) 32%   (f) 51%   (g) $18\frac{1}{2}\%$ (h) $72\frac{1}{2}\%$

3 Write the following decimals as percentages:
   (a) 0.24   (b) 0.3   (c) 0.55   (d) 0.6
   (e) 0.37   (f) 0.235   (g) 0.175   (h) 0.425

4 Write the following fractions as percentages:
   (a) $\frac{9}{10}$ (b) $\frac{3}{10}$ (c) $\frac{3}{5}$ (d) $\frac{1}{5}$
   (e) $\frac{23}{40}$ (f) $\frac{4}{25}$ (g) $\frac{17}{50}$ (h) $\frac{37}{100}$

5 Leo and Geoff took a Maths test. The test was out of 50.
Leo scored 85%, Geoff scored $\frac{3}{4}$ of the marks.
(a) Who scored the higher marks?
(b) Explain your answer.

6 The road tax for a car is £185.
Chris calculates that road tax represents $\frac{1}{10}$ of his annual costs
of running the car, and buying petrol 60%. The remainder of
the costs are insurance and servicing.
(a) How much does Chris spend on insurance and servicing his car?
(b) Write this as a percentage of his total costs.

2.3 Proportion

■ **Two quantities are in proportion if their ratio stays the same
as the quantities get larger or smaller.**

Teaching reference:
(*pp 214–217, section 17.3*)
pp 268–270, section 17.4

Example 5
If 5 videotapes cost £52.50, how much will 3 videotapes cost?

5 videotapes cost £52.50

1 videotape costs $\dfrac{£52.50}{5} = £10.50$

So 3 videotapes cost $3 \times £10.50$
$= £31.50$

Example 6
Six men build a wall in 4 days. How long will it take eight men to
build a similar wall?

6 men take 4 days
1 man would take $6 \times 4 = 24$ days

8 men would take $\dfrac{24}{8} = 3$ days

Exercise 2C — Links (*17D*) 17D

1 Six books cost £36. How much will
(a) one book cost
(b) three books cost?

2 If 5 cinema tickets cost £20, how much will
(a) 1 ticket cost
(b) 8 tickets cost?

3 If 8 cakes cost £3.20, how much will
(a) 3 cakes cost
(b) 10 cakes cost?

4   A recipe for 10 buns has the following ingredients:

>   200 g flour
>   100 g sugar
>   50 g butter

Write down the amount of each ingredient needed for 25 buns.

5   Veronica is going on holiday to France.
She exchanges £100 and receives €161.66.
(a) How many euros would she get for £250?
(b) How much would she have to exchange to get 315 euros?

6   Ross is paid £231.25 for working a 37 hour week.
How much would he be paid if he worked
(a) 40 hours
(b) 30 hours?

7   Eight men can build a garage in 5 days.
How long will it take ten men?

8   A bottle of shampoo lasts a family of five for 1 week.
How long will the same bottle of shampoo last a family of seven?

9   Three gardeners can weed a large garden in 8 hours.
How long would it take four gardeners to weed the same garden?

2.4 Problems involving speed and units of measure

Teaching reference:
(*pp 169–175, 245–247,
sections 13.1, 13.2, 19.6*)
pp 215–221, 302–303,
sections 13.1, 13.2, 19.7

Example 7
A train travels at 100 km per hour.
How far will it travel in 4 hours?

Remember:
100 km per hour means
100 km each hour.

>   The train travels 100 km in 1 hour.
>
>   So it will travel 100×4 km in 4 hours
> $= 400$ km

Example 8
A 3 km race is split into 5 equal stages.
How many metres is each stage?

> $3 \text{ km} = 3 \times 1000 \text{ m}$
> $\qquad = 3000 \text{ m}$
>
>   Each stage $= \dfrac{3000}{5} = 600 \text{ m}$

Example 9

A kilogram is approximately 2.2 pounds.
A baby weighs 8 pounds at birth. Approximately how many kilograms is this?

The baby weighs 8 pounds.

So the baby weighs $\dfrac{8}{2.2} = 3.636\,\text{kg}$ (3 decimal places)

Exercise 2D   Links *(13A–F, 19R)* 13A–F, 19S

1 A runner can run 300 m per minute.
   How far can he run in 5 minutes?

2 A car travels at an average speed of 50 mph (miles per hour).
   How far will the car travel in
   (a) 3 hours   **(b)** 8 hours?

3 In sailing, one knot equals one nautical mile per hour. A boat can sail at an average speed of 10 knots per hour.
   How long will it take the boat to travel
   (a) 50 miles   **(b)** 80 miles   **(c)** 35 miles?

4 A snail crawls at 3 mm per second.
   How long will it take the snail to crawl
   (a) 12 mm   **(b)** 21 mm   **(c)** 150 mm?

5 A 2 litre bottle of cola is shared between 8 children.
   How many millilitres of cola does each child receive?

6 A portion of chips weighs 300 g.
   How many kilograms will 12 portions weigh?

7 A fence is made from six similar fence panels. Each panel is 150 cm long.
   How many metres long is the fence?

8 A pile of 30 exercise books is 12 cm high.
   How thick is each exercise book in mm?

9 A pencil is 6 inches long. 1 inch = 2.5 cm.
   How long is the pencil in cm?

10 Graham puts 8 gallons of petrol into his car. 1 gallon = 4.5 *l*.
   How many litres of petrol did Graham put into his car?

11 Samina is 165 cm tall. 30 cm = 1 foot.
   How tall is Samina in feet?

12 Keith weighs 198 pounds. 1 kg = 2.2 lb.
   How much does Keith weigh in kg?

13 The distance from Manchester to London is 200 miles.
5 miles = 8 km.
Write down the distance from Manchester to London in km.

14 The speed limit in towns is 30 mph. 5 miles = 8 km.
What is the speed limit in towns in km per hour?

Exercise 2E   Mixed questions

1 Paul plants 20 bushes. Four of the bushes die.
What fraction of the bushes
   (a) die   **(b)** survive?

2 Karen is given £25 as a present. She saves £5, spends £12 on
books and the rest on make-up.
What fraction of her present does she spend on
   (a) books   **(b)** make-up?

3 Change the following percentages to **(i)** fractions **(ii)** decimals.
   (a) 30%   **(b)** 90%   **(c)** 35%   **(d)** 85%
   (e) 18%   **(f)** 64%   **(g)** $17\frac{1}{2}$%   **(h)** $42\frac{1}{2}$%

4 Change the following fractions and decimals to percentages:
   (a) $\frac{1}{2}$ **(b)** 0.2   **(c)** $\frac{4}{5}$ **(d)** 0.65
   (e) $\frac{13}{20}$ **(f)** $\frac{14}{25}$ **(g)** $\frac{11}{40}$ **(h)** 0.275

5 Lucy and Jessica were both given £50.
Lucy put 76% of her money into the bank and Jessica put $\frac{3}{4}$ of
her money into the bank.
Who saved the most? Explain your answer.

6 1€ = £0.62
   (a) How many pounds sterling would be exchanged for €55?
   (b) How many euros would be exchanged for £485?

7 A bag of rabbit food lasts 4 rabbits 9 days.
How long will the same bag of rabbit food last
   (a) 3 rabbits   **(b)** 8 rabbits?

8 A train travels at an average speed of 70 km per hour.
   (a) How far will the train travel in
        (i) 4 hours   **(ii)** 10 hours?
   (b) How long will it take the train to travel
        (i) 210 km   **(ii)** 385 km?

9 A brick wall is 1.2 m high. The wall is made from 20 layers of
bricks.
How high is each layer of bricks?

10 A bag of potatoes weighs 11 pounds. 1 kg = 2.2 pounds.
Write down the weight of the bag of potatoes in kilograms.

Summary of key points

■   To write a percentage as a fraction, always use the denominator 100.

■   To write a percentage as a decimal:
- write the percentage as a fraction
- convert the fraction to a decimal
- or simply divide the percentage by 100.

■   To change a decimal to a percentage, multiply the decimal by 100.

■   To write a fraction as a percentage:
- change the fraction to a decimal
- multiply the decimal by 100.

■   Two quantities are in proportion if their ratio stays the same as the quantities get larger or smaller.

3 Linear equations, formulae and sequences

3.1 Solving equations by balancing

Teaching reference:
(*pp 192–194, section 15.1*)

- In an equation, a letter represents a number.
- Solving an equation means finding which number the letter represents. This number is called the *solution* of the equation.
- To rearrange an equation you can
  - add the same quantity to both sides
  - subtract the same quantity from both sides
  - multiply both sides by the same quantity
  - divide both sides by the same quantity.
- Whatever you do to one side of an equation you must do to the other side. This is called the *balance* method.

Example 1
Solve the equation $a + 3 = 7$.

$a = 7 - 3$ Take 3 away from each side.
$a = 4$

-3 is the opposite process of $+3$.

Example 2
Solve the equation $b - 5 = 3$.

$b = 3 + 5$ Add 5 to each side.
$b = 8$

$+5$ is the opposite process of -5.

Example 3
Solve the equation $5c = 15$.
This means $c \times 5 = 15$:

$c = \dfrac{15}{5}$ Divide each side by 5.

$c = 3$

$\dfrac{15}{5}$ means $15 \div 5$.

$\div 5$ is the opposite process of $\times 5$.

Example 4
Solve the equation $\dfrac{d}{6} = 2$.

This means $d \div 6 = 2$:

$d = 2 \times 6$ Multiply each side by 6.
$d = 12$

$\times 6$ is the opposite process of $\div 6$.

Exercise 3A   Links (*15A–15F*) 15A–15F

Solve these equations:

1 $p + 4 = 7$	**2** $a + 7 = 12$	**3** $h + 6 = 15$	**4** $9 + e = 20$
5 $n + 5 = 5$	**6** $3 + g = 8$	**7** $t - 2 = 7$	**8** $u - 5 = 3$
9 $x - 6 = 8$	**10** $v - 7 = 4$	**11** $3d = 24$	**12** $8c = 40$
13 $6q = 42$	**14** $9f = 63$	**15** $7k = 0$	**16** $\dfrac{y}{2} = 5$
17 $\dfrac{r}{6} = 7$	**18** $\dfrac{g}{5} = 9$	**19** $\dfrac{b}{8} = 6$	**20** $\dfrac{m}{7} = 0$

3.2 Equations with two operations

Example 5

Solve the equation $6x + 5 = 23$.

$$6x = 23 - 5 \qquad \text{Take 5 away from each side.}$$
$$6x = 18$$
$$x = \frac{18}{6} \qquad \text{Divide each side by 6.}$$
$$x = 3$$

$\dfrac{18}{6}$ means $18 \div 6$.

■ **The solution of an equation is not always a whole number. It can, for example, be a fraction or a decimal.**

Example 6

Solve the equation $3y - 5 = 9$.

$$3y = 9 + 5 \qquad \text{Add 5 to each side.}$$
$$3y = 14$$
$$y = \frac{14}{3} \qquad \text{Divide each side by 3.}$$
$$y = 4\tfrac{2}{3}$$

Exercise 3B   Links (*15G, 15H*) 15G, 15H

Solve these equations:

1 $2y + 3 = 11$	**2** $3a - 2 = 13$	**3** $4h + 1 = 13$	**4** $5t - 7 = 8$
5 $7d + 5 = 19$	**6** $8c - 1 = 7$	**7** $3u + 8 = 8$	**8** $2v + 1 = 8$
9 $3x - 4 = 1$	**10** $4p + 3 = 10$	**11** $5q - 6 = 7$	**12** $8k + 1 = 20$
13 $10f - 8 = 7$	**14** $5n + 3 = 20$	**15** $6e - 10 = 5$	

3.3 Equations with the letter on both sides

■ You can use the balance method to solve equations with the letter on both sides. You rearrange the equation so that, on one side, there is the letter with a positive number in front of it and, on the other side, there is a number.

Example 7
Solve the equation $6x - 5 = 2x + 7$.
Collect all the x terms on one side:

$4x - 5 = 7$ Take $2x$ away from each side.

Collect the numbers on the other side:

$4x = 12$ Add 5 to each side.
$x = 3$ Divide each side by 4.

> If you took $6x$ away from each side, you would not affect the balance of the equation, but you would get a negative number in front of x.

Example 8
Solve the equation $8y + 7 = 3y + 11$.

$5y + 7 = 11$ Take $3y$ away from each side.
$5y = 4$ Take 7 away from each side.
$y = \frac{4}{5}$ Divide each side by 5.

Exercise 3C   Links (*15M, 15N*) 15N

Solve these equations:

1   $2a + 9 = a + 5$ 2 $3c - 1 = c + 9$
3   $5p - 7 = 2p + 11$ 4 $8b + 9 = 3b + 14$
5   $9q - 8 = 2q + 13$ 6 $x + 13 = 5x + 1$
7   $4d + 17 = 8d - 3$ 8 $7y = 2y + 15$
9   $3n + 14 = 5n$ 10 $5k + 1 = 2k + 1$
11   $4u + 3 = 2u + 8$ 12 $7r - 3 = 2r + 9$
13   $6v - 7 = 3v + 7$ 14 $9t + 5 = 4t + 9$
15   $7m - 2 = 3m + 8$ 16 $3g + 4 = 9g - 1$
17   $5b + 6 = 7b + 5$ 18 $2h + 7 = 8h - 1$
19   $3e = 7e - 18$ 20 $9f = 3f + 4$

3.4 Using word formulae

■ A word formula represents a relationship between quantities using words.

> Teaching reference:
> (*pp 267–268, section 21.1*)

Example 9

This word formula can be used to work out the perimeter of an equilateral triangle:

Perimeter = 3 × length of side

Work out the perimeter of an equilateral triangle with sides of length 9 cm.

Perimeter = 3 × 9 = 27 cm

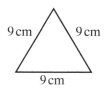

| **Exercise 3D** | **Links (*21A, B*) 21A, B** |

1 This word formula can be used to work out the perimeter of a regular pentagon:

Perimeter = 5 × length of side

Work out the perimeter of a regular pentagon with sides of length 7 cm.

2 Gwen uses this word formula to work out her wage:

Wage = rate per hour × number of hours worked

Gwen's rate per hour is £5 and she worked for 37 hours. Work out her wage.

3 This word formula can be used to work out the perimeter of a rectangle:

Perimeter = 2 × length + 2 × width

Work out the perimeter of a rectangle with a length of 8 cm and a width of 3 cm.

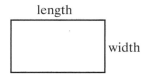

Remember BIDMAS: multiply before you add.

4 Kevin uses this word formula to work out his total pay:

Total pay = rate per hour × number of hours worked + bonus

Kevin's rate per hour is £6; he worked for 35 hours and his bonus was £25.
Work out his total pay.

5 This word formula can be used to work out the area of a triangle:

Area = $\frac{1}{2}$ × base × vertical height

A triangle has a base 8 cm long and a vertical height of 10 cm. Work out the area of the triangle.

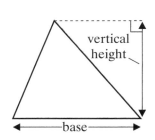

6 Georgina uses this word formula to work out her take-home pay:

Take-home pay =
rate per hour × number of hours worked − deductions

Remember BIDMAS: multiply before you take away.

Georgina's rate per hour is £7; she worked for 40 hours and her deductions were £96. Work out her take-home pay.

7 This word formula can be used to work out the average speed for a journey:

$$\text{Average speed} = \frac{\text{total distance travelled}}{\text{total time taken}}$$

If the distance is in miles and the time is in hours, the average speed is in miles per hour (mph).

Ray travels 215 miles in 5 hours. Work out his average speed.

8 This word formula can be used to work out the angle sum, in degrees, of a polygon:

Angle sum = (number of sides − 2) × 180

Always work brackets out first.

Work out the angle sum of a polygon with 7 sides.

9 This word formula can be used to work out the size, in degrees, of each exterior angle of a regular polygon:

$$\text{Exterior angle} = \frac{360}{\text{number of sides}}$$

Work out the size of each exterior angle of a regular polygon with 8 sides.

10 This word formula can be used to work out the area inside a circle:

Area = π × radius × radius

If you haven't got a π key on your calculator, use 3.14.

Work out the area of a circle with a radius of 4 cm. Give your answer to the nearest whole number.

■ **In a word formula, you can find the value of *any* term, if you know the values of all the other terms.**

Example 10

This word formula can be used to work out the area of a rectangle:

Area = length × width

The area of a rectangle is 63 cm². Its length is 9 cm.
Work out the width of the rectangle.

63 = 9 × width

So width $= \dfrac{63}{9} = 7$ cm

Exercise 3E   **Links** (*21A, B*) **21A, B**

1   This word formula can be used to work out the perimeter of a regular octagon:

    Perimeter = 8 × length of side

    The perimeter of a regular octagon is 56 cm.
    Work out the length of each side.

2   Jan uses this word formula to work out her wage:

    Wage = rate per hour × number of hours worked

    Jan's wage is £198 and her rate per hour is £6. Work out the number of hours she worked.

3   This word formula can be used to work out the perimeter of a rectangle:

    Perimeter = 2 × length + 2 × width

    The perimeter of a rectangle is 34 cm and its length is 10 cm. Work out the width of the rectangle.

4   Ben uses this word formula to work out his total pay:

    Total pay = rate per hour × number of hours worked + bonus

    Ben's total pay is £360; his rate per hour is £10 and he worked for 31 hours. Work out his bonus.

5   This word formula can be used to work out the average speed for a journey:

    $$\text{Average speed} = \frac{\text{total distance travelled}}{\text{total time taken}}$$

    Roy's average speed for a journey was 53 miles per hour. The total time taken for the journey was 3 hours. Work out the total distance he travelled.

6   Liz uses this word formula to work out her take-home pay:

    Take-home pay =
    rate per hour × number of hours worked − deductions

    Liz's take-home pay is £64; her rate per hour is £5 and her deductions are £26. Work out the number of hours she worked.

7   This word formula can be used to work out the volume of a cuboid:

    Volume = length × width × height

    The volume of a cuboid is 90 cm³. Its length is 6 cm and its width is 5 cm. Work out the height of the cuboid.

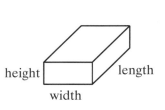

8 This word formula can be used to work out the distance travelled by an object moving at a constant speed:

Distance = speed × time

Hayley walked 10 miles at a constant speed of 4 miles per hour. Work out the time she took.

9 This word formula can be used to work out the roasting time, in minutes, for a joint of lamb:

Roasting time = 20 × weight in lbs + 20

The roasting time for a joint of lamb is 2 hours. Work out the weight of the joint.

> Multiply before you add.

10 This word formula can be used to work out the area of a triangle:

Area = $\frac{1}{2}$ × base × vertical height

A triangle has an area of 20 cm^2 and a base 10 cm long. Work out the vertical height of the triangle.

3.5 Using algebraic formulae

- **A formula is a quick way of expressing a rule.**
- **An algebraic formula uses letters to show a relationship between quantities, $A = lb$, for example.**
- **The letter which appears on its own on the left-hand side of a formula and does not appear on the right-hand side is called the *subject* of the formula.**

> A is the subject of the formula $A = lb$.

Example 11

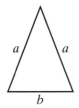

The formula for the perimeter of this isosceles triangle is $P = 2a + b$.
Work out the value of P when $a = 8$ and $b = 5$.

$$P = 2 \times 8 + 5 = 16 + 5 = 21$$

> $2a$ is short for $2 \times a$.

Exercise 3F   **Links (*21E*) (*21C, 21D, 21E*)**

1 The formula for the perimeter of a regular hexagon is $P = 6l$.
Work out the value of P when
   (a) $l = 3$ **(b)** $l = 7$ **(c)** $l = 29$ **(d)** $l = 8.6$

2   The formula for the area of a parallelogram is $A = bh$.
    Work out the value of A when
    (a) $b = 7$ and $h = 3$ **(b)** $b = 9$ and $h = 7$
    (c) $b = 6$ and $h = 3.7$ **(d)** $b = 8.4$ and $h = 4.5$

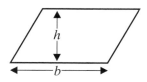

3   The formula for the circumference of a circle is $C = \pi d$.
    Work out, to the nearest whole number, the value of C when
    (a) $d = 2$ **(b)** $d = 5$ **(c)** $d = 3.7$ **(d)** $d = 9.3$

4   The formula for the number of edges a solid has is
    $E = F + V - 2$. Work out the value of E when
    (a) $F = 6$ and $V = 8$ **(b)** $F = 16$ and $V = 9$

5   $y = 2x + 3$ is the equation of a straight line.
    Work out the value of y when
    (a) $x = 4$ **(b)** $x = 6$ **(c)** $x = 10$ **(d)** $x = 7.5$

6   The formula for the perimeter of this isosceles triangle is
    $P = 2a + b$. Work out the value of P when
    (a) $a = 6$ and $b = 4$ **(b)** $a = 12$ and $b = 7$
    (c) $a = 5.3$ and $b = 3.4$ **(d)** $a = 4.7$ and $b = 8.5$

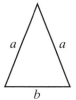

7   The formula $F = 1.8C + 32$ can be used to convert a
    temperature from degrees Celsius to degrees Fahrenheit.
    Work out the value of F when
    (a) $C = 10$ **(b)** $C = 100$ **(c)** $C = 30$ **(d)** $C = 0$

8   The formula for the volume of a cuboid is $V = lwh$.
    Work out the value of V when
    (a) $l = 5$, $w = 4$ and $h = 2$ **(b)** $l = 8$, $w = 5$ and $h = 3$
    (c) $l = 10$, $w = 6$ and $h = 4$ **(d)** $l = 9$, $w = 4$ and $h = 5$

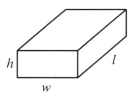

9   The formula $v = u + at$ can be used to work out velocity.
    Work out the value of v when
    (a) $u = 8$, $a = 4$ and $t = 3$ **(b)** $u = 0$, $a = 10$ and $t = 2$
    (c) $u = 7$, $a = 2.6$ and $t = 5$ **(d)** $u = 12$, $a = 10$ and $t = 4.7$

10 The formula $T = 15(W + 1)$ can be used to work out the time
    needed to cook a turkey. Work out the value of T when
    (a) $W = 5$ **(b)** $W = 8$ **(c)** $W = 12$ **(d)** $W = 18$

11 The formula $S = (2n - 4) \times 90$ can be used to work out the
    angle sum, in degrees, of a polygon. Work out the value of S
    when
    (a) $n = 5$ **(b)** $n = 8$ **(c)** $n = 10$ **(d)** $n = 12$

12 The formula $t = \dfrac{d}{s}$ can be used to work out the time taken by
an object moving at a constant speed s to travel a distance d.
Work out the value of t when
(a) $d = 20$ and $s = 4$ (b) $d = 54$ and $s = 9$
(c) $d = 17.4$ and $s = 3$ (d) $d = 32$ and $s = 5$

■ **To find the value of a term which is not the subject of a
formula, put the values you are given into the formula and
solve the resulting equation.**

Example 12

$P = 2a + b$
Work out the value of a when $P = 25$ and $b = 7$.

$25 = 2a + 7$ Solve this equation.
$2a = 18$ Take 7 away from each side.
$a = 9$ Divide each side by 2.

Check:
$2 \times 9 + 7 = 18 + 7$
$= 25$

Exercise 3G

1 $P = 6l$
Work out the value of l when
(a) $P = 24$ (b) $P = 54$ (c) $P = 138$ (d) $P = 35.4$

2 $A = bh$
(a) Work out the value of h when
     (i) $A = 45$ and $b = 5$ (ii) $A = 54$ and $b = 3$
(b) Work out the value of b when
     (i) $A = 35$ and $h = 7$ (ii) $A = 120$ and $h = 8$

3 $E = F + V - 2$
(a) Work out the value of F when
     (i) $E = 9$ and $V = 5$ (ii) $E = 21$ and $V = 9$
(b) Work out the value of V when
     (i) $E = 15$ and $F = 10$ (ii) $E = 30$ and $F = 12$

4 $y = 2x + 3$
Work out the value of x when
(a) $y = 15$ (b) $y = 27$ (c) $y = 10$ (d) $y = 3$

5 $P = 2a + b$
(a) Work out the value of b when
     (i) $P = 15$ and $a = 6$ (ii) $P = 23$ and $a = 4.5$
(b) Work out the value of a when
     (i) $P = 11$ and $b = 5$ (ii) $P = 19$ and $b = 8$

6 $y = 4x - 5$
Work out the value of x when
(a) $y = 3$ (b) $y = 31$ (c) $y = 75$ (d) $y = 6$

7 $V = lwh$
   (a) Work out the value of h when $V = 24$, $l = 3$ and $w = 2$.
   (b) Work out the value of w when $V = 60$, $l = 6$ and $h = 2$.
   (c) Work out the value of l when $V = 80$, $w = 4$ and $h = 5$.

8 $v = u + at$
   (a) Work out the value of u when
        (i) $v = 19$, $a = 7$ and $t = 2$ **(ii)** $v = 25$, $a = 6$ and $t = 3$
   (b) Work out the value of a when $v = 17$, $u = 5$ and $t = 2$.
   (c) Work out the value of t when $v = 31$, $u = 3$ and $a = 7$.

9 $y = \dfrac{x}{5}$
   Work out the value of x when
   (a) $y = 4$ **(b)** $y = 17$ **(c)** $y = 7.4$ **(d)** $y = 0$

10 $t = \dfrac{d}{s}$
   Work out the value of d when
   (a) $t = 3$ and $s = 5$ **(b)** $t = 9$ and $s = 8$
   (c) $t = 7.5$ and $s = 6$ **(d)** $t = 5.6$ and $s = 10$

3.6 Sequences

Teaching reference:
(*pp 34–37, sections 2.10, 2.11*)

■ **A sequence is a succession of numbers formed according to a rule.**

For example, in the sequence 4, 7, 10, …, 4 is the first term and 7 is the second term.

■ **The numbers in a sequence are called the *terms* of the sequence.**

■ **One type of rule for a sequence tells you what to do to each term to obtain the next term in the sequence.**

This is called a 'term to term' rule for the sequence. The term to term rule for the sequence 4, 7, 10, 13, … is **add 3**.

Example 13
The first term in a sequence is 3. The rule for the sequence is **add 5**.

(a) Find the next three terms in the sequence.
(b) Find the tenth term of the sequence.

(a) second term $= \;3 + 5 = 8$
     third term $= \;8 + 5 = 13$
     fourth term $= 13 + 5 = 18$

     The next three terms are 8, 13, 18.

(b) To find the tenth term, you have to add *nine* 5s to 3.
     So tenth term $= 3 + 5 \times 9 = 3 + 45 = 48$

■ **To find the rule for a sequence, it is often helpful to find the *differences* between consecutive terms.**

Example 14

The first five terms of a sequence are 22, 18, 14, 10, 6.
Find the rule for this sequence.

	22		18		14		10		6
differences		4		4		4		4	

Each term is 4 less than the one before it and so the rule is **take 4 away**.

Exercise 3H   Links (2O–S) (2R–V)

1   Find the next three terms for each of these sequences:
   (a) First term = 1; rule is **add 3**.
   (b) First term = 16; rule is **take 5 away**.
   (c) First term = 4; rule is **multiply by 3**.
   (d) First term = 24; rule is **divide by 2**.
   (e) First term = 5; rule is **multiply by 2 then take away 1**.
   (f) First term = 24; rule is **add 8 then divide by 2**.

2   Find the rule for each of these sequences:
   (a) 13, 11, 9, 7, ...   **(b)** 1, 7, 13, 19, ...
   (c) 1000, 100, 10, 1, ...   **(d)** 64, 32, 16, 8, ...

3   The first term of a sequence is 7 and the rule is **add 4**.
   Find the tenth term of the sequence.

4   The first term of a sequence is 35 and the rule is **take 2 away**.
   Find the 15th term of the sequence.

5   The first five terms of a sequence are 5, 7, 9, 11, 13.
   (a) Find the rule for the sequence.
   (b) Find the 20th term of the sequence.

■   **Another type of rule for a sequence tells you what to do to the term number to obtain that term in the sequence.**

> This is called a 'position to term' rule for the sequence.

Example 15

The rule for a sequence is **multiply the term number by 5 and add 2**.
Find the first four terms of the sequence.

The first term is term number 1. So first term = $1 \times 5 + 2 = 7$.

Similarly, second term = $2 \times 5 + 2 = 12$
third term = $3 \times 5 + 2 = 17$
fourth term = $4 \times 5 + 2 = 22$

> Notice that the differences between the terms are all 5.

The first four terms are 7, 12, 17, 22.

Example 16

The rule for a sequence is **take 2 away from the term number and multiply by 5**. Find the ninth term.

The ninth term is term number 9.

So ninth term $= (\mathbf{9} - 2) \times 5$
$= 7 \times 5$
$= 35$

Exercise 3I	**Links (2W)**

1   For each of these rules, find:
   (a) the first three terms of the sequence,
   (b) the tenth term of the sequence.
       (i)   Add 9 to the term number.
       (ii) Multiply the term number by 7.
       (iii) Multiply the term number by 4 and take 1 away.
       (iv) Add 3 to the term number and multiply by 2.
       (v)   Multiply the term number by 6 and add 5.

2   The rule for a sequence is **take 4 away from the term number and multiply by 10**. Find the twelfth term.

3   The rule for a sequence is **divide the term number by 2 and add 9**. Find the 22nd term.

4   Find the rule for each of these sequences:
   (a) 5, 6, 7, 8, . . .   **(b)** 5, 10, 15, 20, . . .
   (c) 8, 16, 24, 32, . . .   **(d)** 0, 1, 2, 3, . . .

5   Find the rule for each of these sequences:
   (a) 8, 11, 14, 17, . . .   **(b)** 1, 7, 13, 19, . . .
   (c) 8, 12, 16, 20, . . .   **(d)** 0, 8, 16, 24, . . .

Example 17

Here are the first three shapes in a sequence of shapes made from matchsticks:

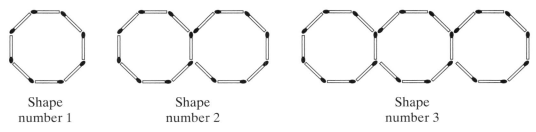

Shape number 1	Shape number 2	Shape number 3

(a) (i) Draw shape number 4.
    (ii) Find the number of matchsticks in shape number 4.

(b) Work out the number of matchsticks in
   (i) shape number 5,
   (ii) shape number 12.

(a) (i)

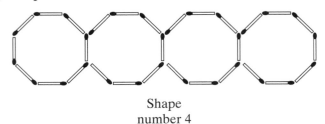

Shape
number 4

   (ii) 29 matchsticks.
(b) (i) The table shows the number of matchsticks in each of the
        first four shapes.

Shape number	1	2	3	4
Number of matchsticks	8	15	22	29

$$8 \qquad 15 \qquad 22 \qquad 29$$
differences $\quad$ 7 $\qquad$ 7 $\qquad$ 7

In shape number 5, there are $29 + 7 = 36$ matchsticks.
   (ii) In shape number 12, there are $8 + 7 \times 11 = 85$ matchsticks.

> In shape number 5, there are $8 + 7 \times \mathbf{4}$ matchsticks.

Exercise 3J   Links (2W)

1   Here are the first four shapes in a sequence of shapes made
      from matchsticks:

   Shape   Shape   Shape   Shape
number 1   number 2   number 3   number 4

   (a) (i) Draw shape number 5.
      (ii) Find the number of matchsticks in shape number 5.
   (b) Work out the number of matchsticks in
      (i) shape number 6,   **(ii)** shape number 15.

2   Here are the first four shapes in a sequence made from
      matchsticks:

  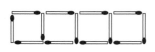

   Shape   Shape   Shape   Shape
number 1   number 2   number 3   number 4

(a) Draw shape number 5.
(b) Complete the table:

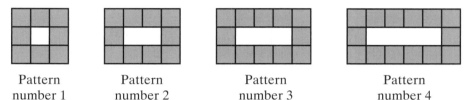

Shape number	1	2	3	4	5	6
Number of matchsticks	4	7	10	13		

(c) Work out the number of matchsticks in shape number 21.

3   Here are the first four patterns in a sequence of patterns made with square tiles:

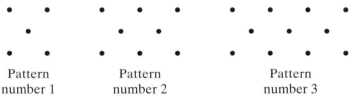

Pattern number 1   Pattern number 2   Pattern number 3   Pattern number 4

(a) (i) Draw pattern number 5.
    (ii) Find the number of tiles in pattern number 5.
(b) Work out the number of tiles in
    (i) pattern number 6,   (ii) pattern number 17.

4   Here are the first three patterns in a sequence of patterns made from dots:

Pattern number 1   Pattern number 2   Pattern number 3

(a) Draw pattern number 4.
(b) Complete the table:

Pattern number	1	2	3	4	5
Number of dots	5	8	11		

(c) Work out the number of dots in pattern number 25.

5   Here are the first four patterns in a sequence of patterns made with square tiles:

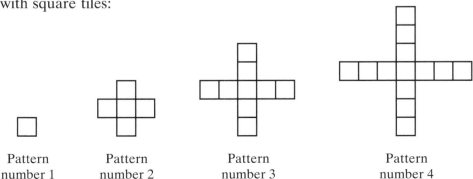

Pattern number 1   Pattern number 2   Pattern number 3   Pattern number 4

(a) (i) Draw pattern number 5.
    (ii) Find the number of tiles in pattern number 5.
(b) Work out the number of tiles in
    (i) pattern number 6,   (ii) pattern number 15.

1 Solve these equations:

(a) $a + 8 = 13$ (b) $9b = 36$ (c) $c - 7 = 3$ (d) $\dfrac{d}{4} = 8$

2 Solve these equations:
(a) $3a + 2 = 20$ (b) $4b - 1 = 27$ (c) $2c + 5 = 6$ (d) $5d - 4 = 3$

3 Solve these equations:
(a) $3a + 5 = a + 11$ (b) $7b - 2 = 4b + 13$
(c) $5c - 9 = 2c - 7$ (d) $3d + 10 = 9d - 11$

4 This word formula can be used to work out the total cost, in pounds, of running a car:

$$\text{Total cost} = \text{fixed costs} + \frac{\text{number of miles travelled}}{6}$$

(a) Flora's fixed costs were £500 and she travelled 9000 miles.
    Work out her total cost.
(b) Harry's total cost was £2700 and he travelled 12 000 miles.
    Work out his fixed costs.
(c) Alison's total cost was £1600 and her fixed costs were
    £400. Work out the number of miles she travelled.

5 The formula $v = u - gt$ can be used to work out velocity.
(a) Work out the value of v when $u = 45$, $g = 10$ and $t = 3$.
(b) Work out the value of u when $v = 8$, $g = 10$ and $t = 2$.

6 The formula $A = l \times l$ can be used to work out
the area of a square.
Work out the value of A when $l = 9$.

$l \times l$ is often written as l^2.

7 The formula $P = 2(l + b)$ can be used to work out the
perimeter of a rectangle. Work out the value of P when
(a) $l = 9$ and $b = 4$ (b) $l = 6.7$ and $b = 3.4$

8 The formula $C = \dfrac{(F - 32) \times 5}{9}$ can be used to convert a
temperature from degrees Fahrenheit to degrees Celsius.
Work out the value of C when
(a) $F = 59$ (b) $F = 104$ (c) $F = 32$ (d) $F = 212$

9 The formula $d = \dfrac{a+b}{3}$ can be used to work out the distance apart two bushes should be planted.

    (a) Work out the value of d when $a = 50$ and $b = 43$.

    (b) Work out the value of b when $d = 29$ and $a = 59$.

10 Here are the first three shapes in a sequence of shapes made from matchsticks:

  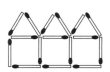

    Shape   Shape   Shape

   number 1   number 2   number 3

  (a) **(i)** Draw shape number 4.

        (ii) Find the number of matchsticks in shape number 4.

  (b) Work out the number of matchsticks in

        (i) shape number 5,   **(ii)** shape number 17.

Summary of key points

- ■ In an equation, a letter represents a number.

- ■ Solving an equation means finding which number the letter represents. This number is called the *solution* of the equation.

- ■ To rearrange an equation you can
    - add the same quantity to both sides
    - subtract the same quantity from both sides
    - multiply both sides by the same quantity
    - divide both sides by the same quantity.

- ■ Whatever you do to one side of an equation you must do to the other side. This is called the *balance* method.

- ■ The solution of an equation is not always a whole number. It can, for example, be a fraction or a decimal.

- ■ You can use the balance method to solve equations with the letter on both sides. You rearrange the equation so that, on one side, there is the letter with a positive number in front of it and, on the other side, there is a number.

- ■ A word formula represents a relationship between quantities using words.

- ■ In a word formula, you can find the value of *any* term, if you know the values of all the other terms.

- ■ A formula is a quick way of expressing a rule.

- ■ An algebraic formula uses letters to show a relationship between quantities.

- The letter which appears on its own on the left-hand side of a formula and does not appear on the right-hand side is called the *subject* of the formula.

- To find the value of a term which is not the subject of a formula, put the values you are given into the formula and solve the resulting equation.

- A sequence is a succession of numbers formed according to a rule.

- The numbers in a sequence are called the *terms* of the sequence.

- One type of rule for a sequence tells you what to do to each term to obtain the next term in the sequence.

  This is called a 'term to term' rule for the sequence.

- To find the rule for a sequence, it is often helpful to find the *differences* between consecutive terms.

- Another type of rule for a sequence tells you what to do to the term number to obtain that term in the sequence.

  This is called a 'position to term' rule for the sequence.

4 Mensuration

4.1 Perimeter

■ **The perimeter of a shape is the distance around the edge of the shape.**

Example 1

Work out the perimeter of this shape. All the corners are right angles.

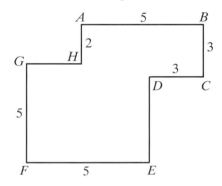

You do not know the length of *GH* or *DE*.

$$GH + AB = EF + CD \quad \text{(the width of the shape)}$$
$$GH + 5 = 5 + 3$$
$$GH = 3$$

Also $\quad FG + AH = DE + BC \quad$ (the height of the shape)
$$5 + 2 = DE + 3$$
$$DE = 4$$

Perimeter $= 5 + 3 + 3 + 4 + 5 + 5 + 3 + 2 = 30$

Exercise 4A   **Links (*19A*) 19A**

Work out the perimeter of these shapes:

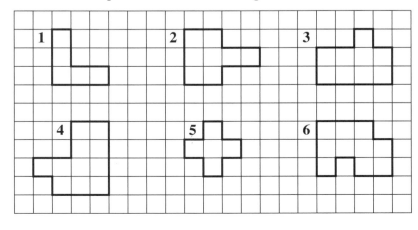

Width of each
square $= 1$

In questions **7**, **8** and **9** the corners are right angles.

7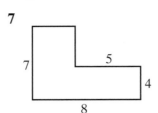

8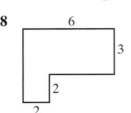

9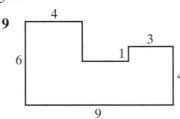

10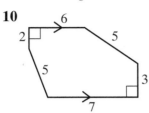

11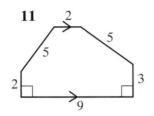

4.2 Area

Teaching reference:
(*pp 235–237, section 19.2*)
pp 288–290, section 19.2

The area of a shape is a measure of the amount of space it covers.

Example 2

Estimate the area of the shape drawn on this grid of centimetre squares.

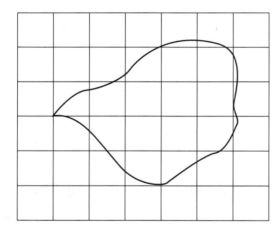

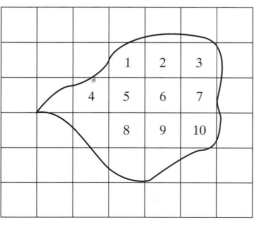

There are 10 complete or almost complete squares. The other pieces are enough to make about 3 squares.

Area $= 13 \, \text{cm}^2$

Exercise 4B   Links (*19B*) 19B

1–11 Work out the area of the shapes in **Exercise 4A**.
In questions **10** and **11** you may find it helpful to draw the
shapes on squared paper.

In questions **12–14**, estimate the area.

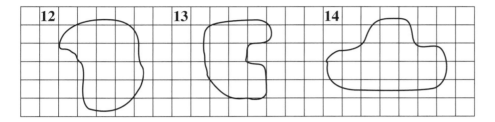

■ **Area of a rectangle = length × width**
$$A = lw$$

The formula still works when length and width are not whole
numbers.

Example 3
Work out the area of the rectangle:

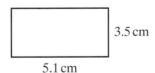

5.1 cm

3.5 cm

in centimetres: in millimetres:
$5.1 \times 3.5 = 17.85$ $51 \times 35 = 1785$
area $= 17.85 \, \text{cm}^2$ area $= 1785 \, \text{mm}^2$

Example 4
The area of a rectangle is $240 \, \text{m}^2$.
The length is 15 m.
Work out the width.

Area = length × width
$240 = 15 \times$ width

So, width $= 240 \div 15 = 16 \, \text{m}$.

34   Mensuration

Exercise 4C   **Links 19K**

Work out the area of these rectangles:

1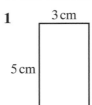

2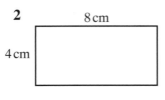

3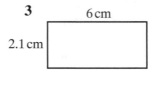

4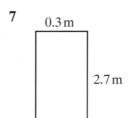

5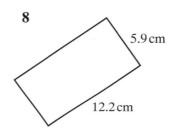

6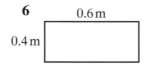

7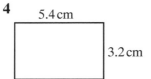

8

In the following questions work out the length of the rectangle:

9

10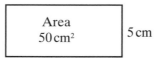

11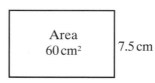

12

13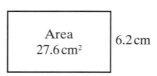

14

15

4.3 Area of triangles, trapeziums and composite shapes

- **Area of a triangle**
  = $\frac{1}{2}$ × base × vertical height

  $A = \frac{1}{2}bh$

- **Area of a parallelogram**
  = base × vertical height

  $A = bh$

- **Area of a trapezium**
  = $\frac{1}{2}$ × sum of parallel sides
      × distance between parallel sides

  $A = \frac{1}{2}(a + b)h$

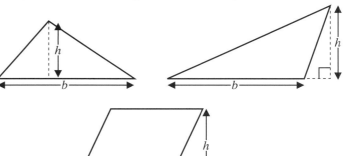

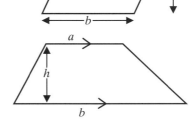

Example 5

Work out the area of the trapezium:

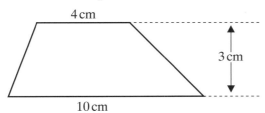

The shape is made from two triangles:

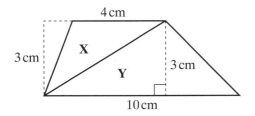

Area **X** $= \frac{1}{2} \times 4 \times 3 = 6\,\text{cm}^2$

Area **Y** $= \frac{1}{2} \times 10 \times 3 = 15\,\text{cm}^2$

Area $= 6 + 15 = 21\,\text{cm}^2$

or use the formula:

$A = \frac{1}{2}(4 + 10) \times 3 = 21\,\text{cm}^2$

Exercise 4D   **Links 19K, 19L**

Find the areas of these triangles:

1   **2**   **3**   **4**

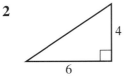
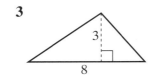

Find the areas of these parallelograms:

5
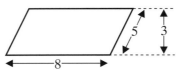

6
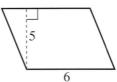

7
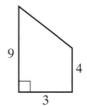

Find the areas of these trapeziums:

8
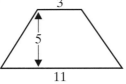

9
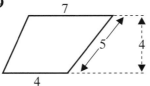

10
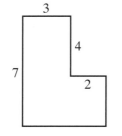

Find the areas of these composite shapes. The corners are right angles in questions **11** and **12**.

11
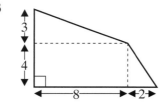

12
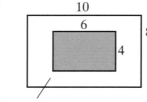

13
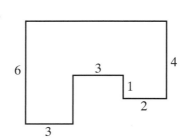

14
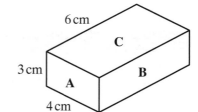
Find this area

15
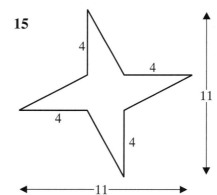

4.4 Surface area of cuboids

Example 6

Find the surface area of this cuboid:

End face   **A** $= 3 \times 4 = 12\,\text{cm}^2$
Front face **B** $= 6 \times 3 = 18\,\text{cm}^2$
Top face   **C** $= 6 \times 4 = 24\,\text{cm}^2$

Opposite faces have the same area:

Two ends $= 24\,\text{cm}^2$; front and back $= 36\,\text{cm}^2$; top and bottom $= 48\,\text{cm}^2$.

Total surface area $= 108\,\text{cm}^2$

Exercise 4E

1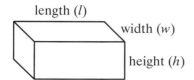

Work out the total surface area for the cuboids:

	Length	Width	Height	Surface area
(a)	4	7	2	
(b)	16	8	3	
(c)	21	4	5	
(d)	16	3	2	
(e)	10	5	3	

4.5 Volume of cuboids

Example 7

Work out the volume of the cuboid (each small cube is
$1\,\text{cm} \times 1\,\text{cm} \times 1\,\text{cm}$):

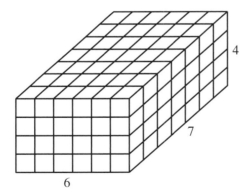

Counting the cubes:

The number of cubes in the bottom layer $= 6 \times 7 = 42$
The cuboid has 4 layers:
number of cubes $= 4 \times 42 = 168$
Volume $= 168\,\text{cm}^3$

■ **Volume of a cuboid = length × width × height**
$$V = lwh$$

■ **Volume of a cube is given by $V = l^3$.**

Exercise 4F   **Links 19J, 19P**

1   Work out the number of cubes in each of these cuboids:

(a) 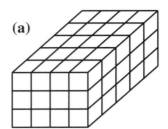   (b) 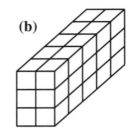   (c)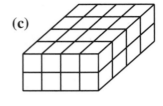

2   Work out the volumes of these cuboids:

(a)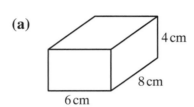

4 cm
8 cm
6 cm

(b)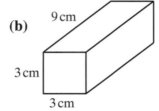

9 cm
3 cm
3 cm

(c)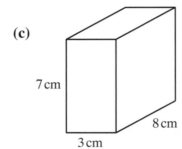

7 cm
3 cm
8 cm

3   Work out the volumes of these cuboids:

(a)

2.6 cm
4.2 cm
3.1 cm

(b)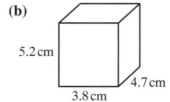

5.2 cm
4.7 cm
3.8 cm

(c)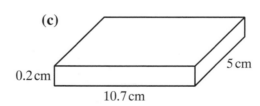

0.2 cm
5 cm
10.7 cm

4   Copy and complete the table:

	Length	Width	Height	Volume
(a)	2 m	3 m	5 m	
(b)	2 m	4 m		40 m³
(c)		6 m	3 m	72 m³
(d)	5 m		8 m	200 m³
(e)		4 m	5 m	30 m³
(f)	8 m	3 m		60 m³
(g)	50 cm		4 cm	40 cm³
(h)		6 cm	0.5 cm	1.2 cm³

5 Find the volumes of these shapes which are made from cuboids:

(a)

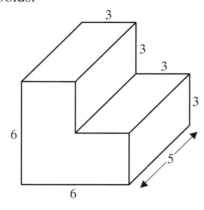
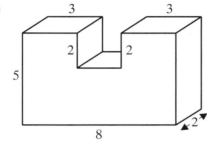

(b)

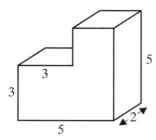

(c)

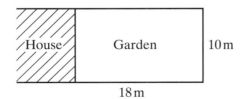

Exercise 4G   **Links (19Q)19Q**

1 A swimming pool measures 10 m by 4 m. It is surrounded by a path made from square slabs 50 cm by 50 cm. The path goes all the way round and is 1 m wide. How many slabs are used?

2 Carpet tiles are 60 cm by 60 cm. They are sold in packs of 10. How many packs are required to cover the floor of a room which measures 4.8 m by 4.2 m?

3 Fencing panels are 2 m long and cost £12.99 each.
Work out the cost for the fencing panels to surround three sides of a garden as shown:

House Garden 10 m

18 m

4 Water weighs 1 gram for each cubic centimetre.
Work out the weight of water in a full fish tank which measures 45 cm by 20 cm by 25 cm.

5   A drink dispenser is in the shape of a cuboid with base 40 cm by 18 cm. Each drink served is 220 m*l*. During the morning the level drops from 23 cm to 12 cm. How many drinks have been served?

6   Metric bricks are 20 cm long by 10 cm high.
    How many bricks are required to build a wall 6 m long and 1.2 m high?

7   A box of matches measures 5 cm by $3\frac{1}{2}$ cm by $1\frac{1}{2}$ cm. How many boxes of matches can be packed into a container which measures 25 cm by 35 cm by 15 cm?
    (Hint: a row of 5 matchboxes is 25 cm long.)

8   Bicycle inner tubes are packed into boxes which measure 8 cm by 9 cm by 4 cm. How many boxes of inner tubes will fit into a carton which measures 32 cm by 45 cm by 20 cm?

9   A packet of washing powder measures 6 cm by 16 cm by 23 cm. How many packets of washing powder can be packed in a carton which measures 46 cm by 36 cm by 64 cm?

Summary of key points

■ **The perimeter of a shape is the distance around the edge of the shape.**

■ **The area of a shape is a measure of the amount of space it covers.**

■ **Area of a rectangle = length × width**
$$A = lw$$

■ **Area of a triangle = $\frac{1}{2}$ × base × height**
$$A = \tfrac{1}{2}bh$$

■ **Area of a parallelogram = base × vertical height**
$$A = bh$$

■ **Area of a trapezium =**
$\frac{1}{2}$ × sum of parallel sides × distance beteen parallel sides
$$A = \tfrac{1}{2}(a+b)h$$

■ **Volume of a cuboid = length × width × height**
$$V = lwh$$

■ **Volume of a cube is given by $V = l^3$.**

5 Angles

5.1 Angles on a straight line

■ The angles on a straight line add up to 180°.

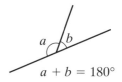

$a + b = 180°$

Example 1

Work out angle x.

$$x + 15 + 32 = 180$$
$$x + 47 = 180$$
$$x = 180 - 47 = 133$$

ABC is a straight line

Exercise 5A   **Links** (*3F*) **3F**

In these questions work out the size of the marked angles:

1

2

3

4

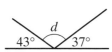

5

6

7

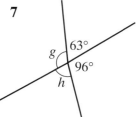

8

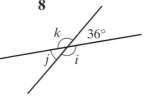

5.2 Angles meeting at a point

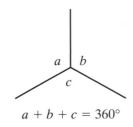

■ The angles meeting at a point add up to 360°.

$$a + b + c = 360°$$

■ Where two straight lines cross, the opposite angles are equal. They are called *vertically opposite angles*.

$$x = y$$

Example 2
Work out angles p and q.

$p = 38$ (opposite angles)
$90 + p + q = 180$ (angles on a straight line)
$90 + 38 + q = 180$
$q = 180 - 90 - 38 = 52°$

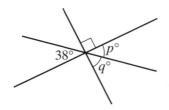

Exercise 5B   **Links (3G) 3G**

In these questions, find the angles marked by letters:

1

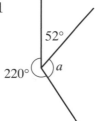

52°
220° a

2

170° b 120°

3

c 130°

4

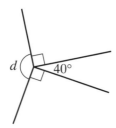

d 40°

5

60°
35°
e 27°

6

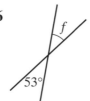

f
53°

7

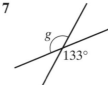

g
133°

8

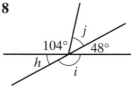

104° j 48°
h i

9 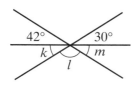   **10**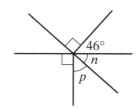

5.3 Angle properties of triangles

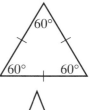

■   **In an equilateral triangle all angles are 60°.**

■   **In an isosceles triangle two angles and two sides are equal.**

■   **The interior angles of a triangle always add up to 180°.**

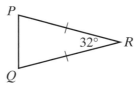

$a + b + c = 180°$

Example 3

Work out the missing angles in these isosceles triangles:

(a) 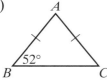   (b)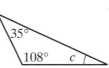

(a) angle $B = 52°$
     angle $C = 52°$

     angle $A = 180 - 52 - 52$
     angle $A = 76°$

(b) angle $R = 32°$
     angle $P +$ angle $Q = 180 - 32$
     $\qquad\qquad\qquad = 148°$
     angle $P =$ angle $Q = 74°$

Exercise 5C   **Links (3H) 3H**

In these questions work out the marked angles:

1 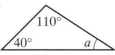   **2**   **3** 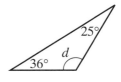   **4**

5

f
$63°$ e

6
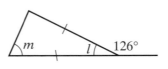
$112°$ g

7

h

8

i $49°$

9
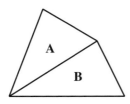
k
$114°$ j

10
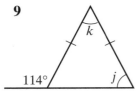
m l $126°$

5.4 Angles of a quadrilateral

■ **The interior angles of a quadrilateral always add up to 360°.**

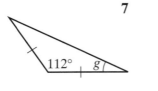
A
B

Angles in triangle **A** = 180°
Angles in triangle **B** = 180°
Angles in the quadrilateral = 360°

Example 4

Work out angles (a) x, (b) y and (c) z.

(a) $70 + 66 + 135 + x = 360$ (angles in a quadrilateral)
$x = 360 - 70 - 66 - 135$
$= 89°$

(b) $y + 135 = 180$ (angles on a straight line)
$y = 180 - 135 = 45°$

(c) $\angle DBC = \angle BCD = z$ (triangle BDC is isosceles)
$2z + y = 2z + 45 = 180$ (angles in a triangle)
$2z = 180 - 45 = 135$ $z = 67\frac{1}{2}°$

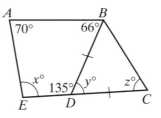
A B
$70°$ $66°$
$x°$ $135°$ $y°$ $z°$
E D C

Exercise 5D **Links** (*3H*) **3H**

In these questions work out the marked angles:

1
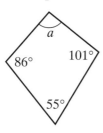
a
$86°$ $101°$
$55°$

2
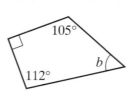
$105°$
$112°$ b

3

c
$46°$

4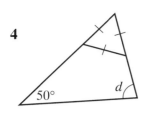

5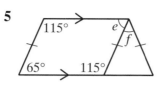

6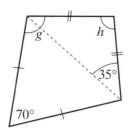

7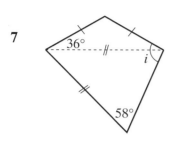

8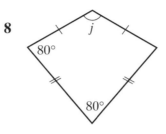

Example 5

Find the angles in this triangle:

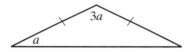

Because the triangle is isosceles, the unmarked angle must be a.

So $a + a + 3a = 180$
$$5a = 180$$
$$a = 36°$$

The angles must be 36°, 36° and 108°.

Exercise 5E   **Mixed questions**

In questions **1–6** find the value of the letter:

1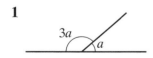

2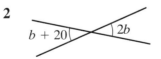

3

4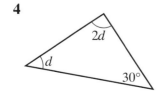

5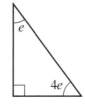

6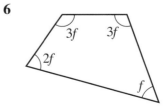

7 Work out ∠*ADB*:

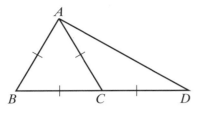
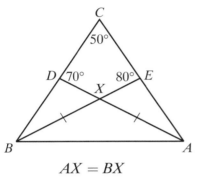

8

Diagram NOT
accurately drawn.

AX = BX

(a) Find ∠*XBA*.
(b) Explain why triangle *CEB* is isosceles.

Anyone who answers questions **7** and **8** correctly has done very well.

Summary of key points

■ **Angles on a straight line add up to 180°.**

$a + b = 180°$

■ **The angles meeting at a point add up to 360°.**

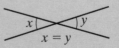

$a + b + c = 360°$

■ **Where two straight lines cross, the opposite angles are equal. They are called *vertically opposite angles*.**

$x = y$

■ **In an equilateral triangle all angles are 60°.**
■ **In an isosceles triangle two angles and two sides are equal.**
■ **The interior angles of a triangle always add up to 180°.**
■ **The interior angles of a quadrilateral always add up to 360°.**

6 Two-dimensional shapes

6.1 Congruent shapes

■ **Shapes which are exactly the same size and shape are congruent.**

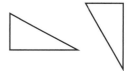

Example 1
Which of these shapes are congruent?

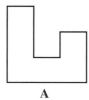 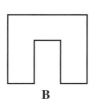  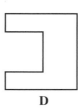

A   B   C   D

Shapes **A** and **C** are congruent.
They have the same length sides and same size angles.

Example 2
Write down the letters of two pairs of congruent shapes:

 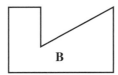 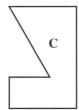

  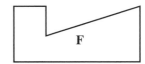

Shapes **A** and **E** are congruent.
Shapes **C** and **B** are congruent.

Reflected shapes are still
the same size and shape.
This is why **A** and **E** are
congruent.

Exercise 6A   **Links (5D) 5D**

In questions **1–5**, write down the letters of the shapes which are congruent:

1

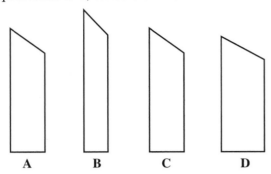

A   B   C   D

2

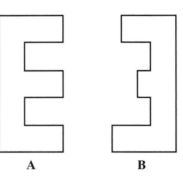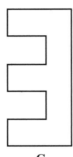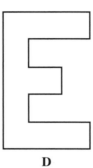

A   B   C   D

3

A

B

C

D

4

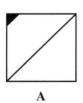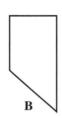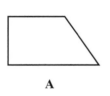

A   B   C   D

5

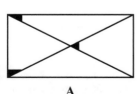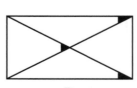

A

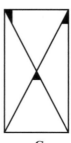

B   C

D

6 Write down the letters of two pairs of congruent shapes:

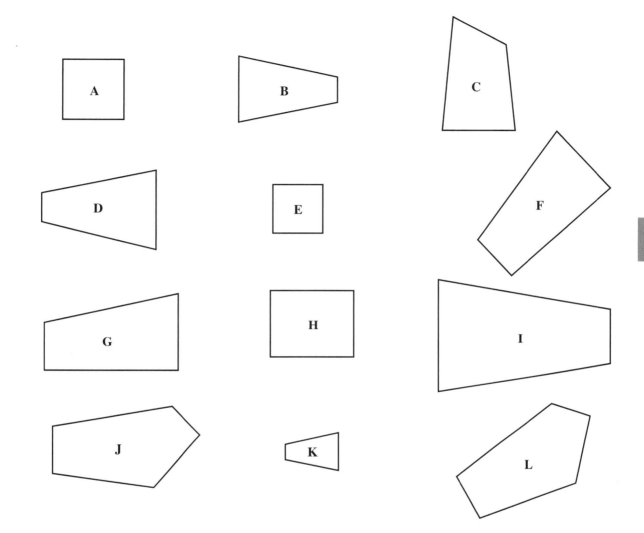

6.2 Polygons

■ **A polygon is a 2-D shape with straight sides.**

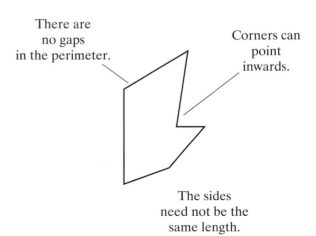

There are
no gaps
in the perimeter.

Corners can
point
inwards.

The sides
need not be the
same length.

■ **A polygon is a regular polygon if its sides are all the same length and its angles are all the same size.**

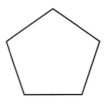

Regular
pentagon

Regular
hexagon

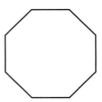

Regular
octagon

■ **For a polygon: interior angle + exterior angle = 180°.**

■ **The exterior angles of a polygon always add up to 360°.**

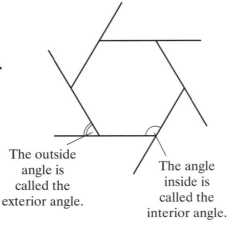

The outside
angle is
called the
exterior angle.

The angle
inside is
called the
interior angle.

Example 3

Work out: (a) the exterior angle of a regular octagon,
           (b) the interior angle of a regular octagon.

(a) A regular octagon has 8 sides.
    There are 8 equal exterior angles.

$$\text{So each exterior angle} = 360 \div 8$$
$$= 45°$$

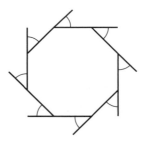

(b) Each interior angle $= 180° - 45°$
                        $= 135°$

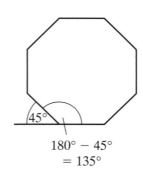

45°

$180° - 45°$
$= 135°$

Example 4

Work out the missing angle for this polygon:

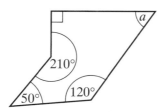

The interior angles are made by 3 triangles
so sum of interior angles $= 180° \times 3$
$$= 540°$$

The angles given $= 120° + 50° + 210° + 90°$
$$= 470°$$

So missing angle $a = 540° - 470°$
$$= 70°$$

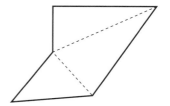

Example 5

The exterior angle of a regular polygon is $60°$.
Work out the number of sides.

Sum of exterior angles $= 360°$
So number of sides $= 360 \div 60 = 6$ sides

Exercise 6B   Links (5F) 5E

1   Work out:
    (a) the exterior angle of a regular 9-sided polygon,
    (b) the interior angle of a regular 9-sided polygon.

2   Work out:
    (a) the exterior angle of a regular hexagon,
    (b) the interior angle of a regular hexagon.

3   The exterior angle of a regular polygon is $30°$.
    Work out the number of sides.

4   The interior angle of a regular polygon is $162°$.
    (a) Work out the exterior angle.
    (b) Work out how many sides it has.

5   Draw a regular octagon with 5 cm sides.
    • Join all the vertices.
    • Identify different congruent shapes and say how many of
      each of them there are.

6 Work out the missing angle for each polygon:

(a)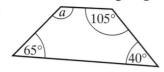

(b)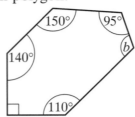

(c)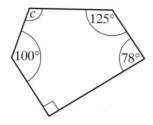

(d)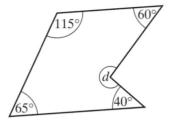

6.3 Tessellations

■ **A pattern of shapes which fit together without leaving any gaps or overlapping is called a *tessellation*.**

Example 6
Tessellate this shape:

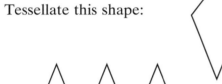

Here is one possible way. The tessellation must have at least six shapes.

Example 7
Show how a regular hexagon can tessellate.

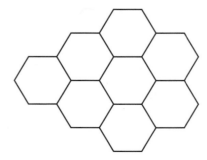

Exercise 6C   Links (5G) 5H

You may find squared or dotted paper useful in this exercise.

1   Show how these shapes tessellate:

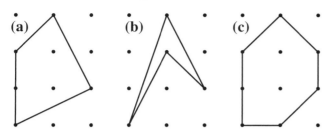

2   Show how a square and an octagon can tessellate.

3   Design a pattern of at least 2 shapes that tessellate.

6.4 Construction activity

Use a pair of compasses to
draw a circle, centre *A*, radius
5 cm.

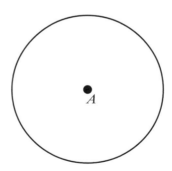

With the same radius and centre
on the circumference of this
circle, draw a second circle,
centre *B*.

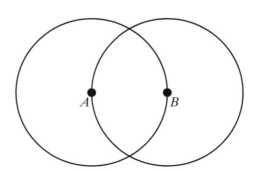

Join A, B and C to make a
triangle. Do the same with
A, B and D. Explain why ABC
and ABD are equilateral triangles.

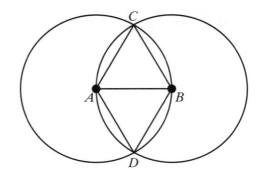

Extend BA, CA and DA to
complete the diameters of the circle.
$BDEFGC$ is a regular hexagon.
Why?

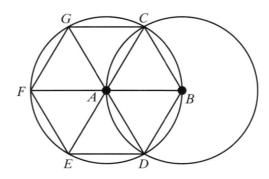

Use a straight edge and a set square
to confirm GC, FB and ED are parallel.
What other lines are parallel?

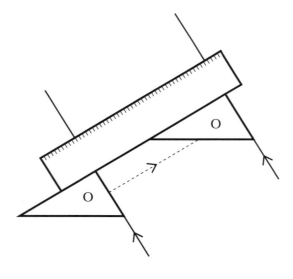

Slide the set square along
a straight edge to check
or draw parallel lines.

You can use the fact that equal angles at the centre of a circle
make chords of equal length to create regular polygons in a circle.

For an octagon the centre angles
are $\dfrac{360}{8} = 45°$

For a pentagon the centre angles
are $\dfrac{360}{5} = 72°$

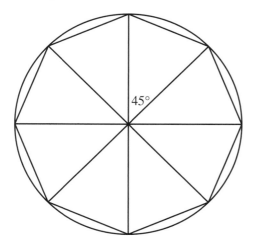

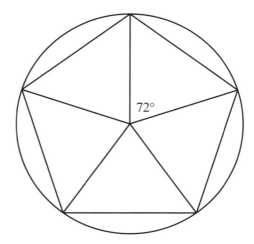

You can construct an accurate triangle with ruler and compasses
when told the length of its sides.

Example 8
Construct an accurate triangle with sides 3 cm, 5 cm and 6 cm.

Step 1
Draw one of the
sides (usually the
longest is best):

Step 2
Set the compasses
at 3 cm, and with
the centre at one
end of the line,
draw an arc:

Step 3
Set the compasses
at 5 cm and draw
an arc from the
other end of the
line:

Step 4
Complete
the
triangle:

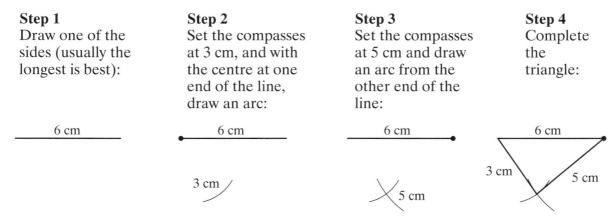

Exercise 6D	**Links (5A, B) 5B, C**

1 Construct accurate drawings of these triangles:

(a)

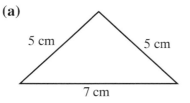

(b)

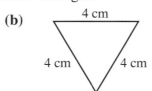

(c)

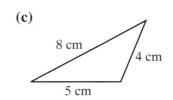

2   Construct accurate drawings of the following triangles:
   (a) triangle ABC with $AB = 5$ cm, $BC = 6$ cm and $CA = 7$ cm
   (b) triangle PQR with $PQ = 4$ cm, $QR = 6$ cm and $RP = 8$ cm
   (c) a triangle with sides 4 cm, 7 cm and 8 cm
   (d) a triangle with sides $5\frac{1}{2}$ cm, 6 cm and $6\frac{1}{2}$ cm.

Summary of key points

- Shapes which are exactly the same size and shape are congruent.

- A polygon is a 2-D shape with straight sides.

- A polygon is a regular polygon if its sides are all the same length and its angles are all the same size.

- For a polygon: interior angle + exterior angle = 180°.

- The exterior angles of a polygon always add up to 360°.

- A pattern of shapes which fit together without leaving any gaps or overlapping is called a *tessellation*.

7 Transformations

7.1 Translation

- **A translation moves every point on a shape the same distance in the same direction.**

- **To describe a translation fully you need to give the distance moved and the direction of the movement.**

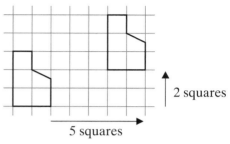

5 squares

2 squares

Notice the shape stays the same (it is congruent).

Example 1

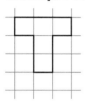

Translate this shape by 3 squares right and 4 squares up.

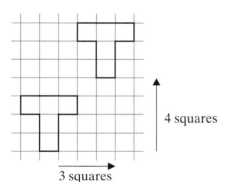

All the vertices (corners) have moved exactly the same amount.

4 squares

3 squares

Example 2

The triangle *ABC* is shown on the grid.

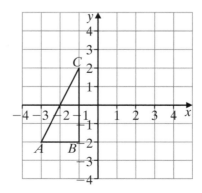

(a) Write down the coordinates of *ABC*.

ABC is translated to *A'B'C'* by the translation that moves *A* to *A'* (0, −3).

(b) Plot *A'* and draw the image *A'B'C'*.

(a) $A(-3, -2)$, $B(-1, -2)$, $C(-1, 2)$

(b)

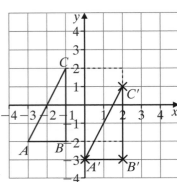

ABC is the object.
A'B'C' is the image.

Check *A'B'C'* is correct by tracing *ABC* and sliding it from *ABC* to *A'B'C'*.

Example 3

Describe the translation for this object–image pair:

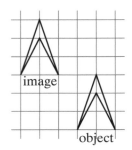

each point moves

So the translation is 3 squares left and 3 squares up.

Exercise 7A   Links (22A) 22A

1   Draw each shape on squared paper and translate it by the amount shown:

(a)

3 squares left

(b)

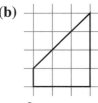

2 squares up

(c)

2 squares left
3 squares up

(d)

4 squares right
2 squares down

(e)

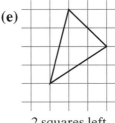

2 squares left
2 squares down

(f)

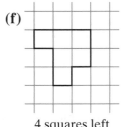

4 squares left
3 squares up

(g)

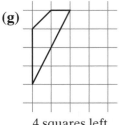

4 squares left
2 squares down

2 For each of parts (**i**) to (**iv**), copy the grid and answer (**a**) and (**b**):
 (**a**) Write down the coordinates of *A*, *B*, *C* and *D*.
   ABCD is translated to *A'B'C'D'* by the translation that
   moves *A* to *A'* (1, −2).
 (**b**) Plot *A'* and draw the image *A'B'C'D'*.

(**i**)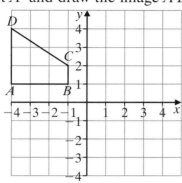

(**ii**)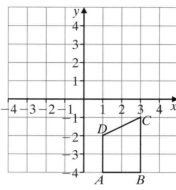

(**iii**)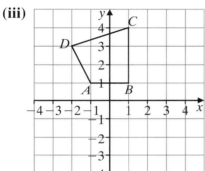

(**iv**)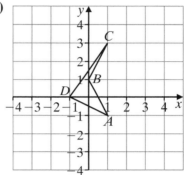

3 Describe the translation for each object–image pair:

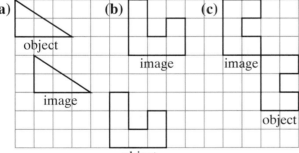

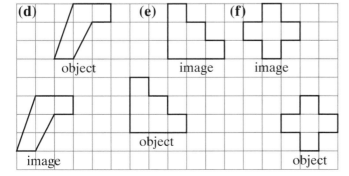

7.2 Enlargement

- **In an enlargement all angles stay the same and lengths are changed in the same proportion.**
- **The scale factor is a multiplier for lengths.**
- **The centre of enlargement determines the final position of the enlarged figure.**
- **In an enlargement image lines are parallel to their corresponding object lines.**

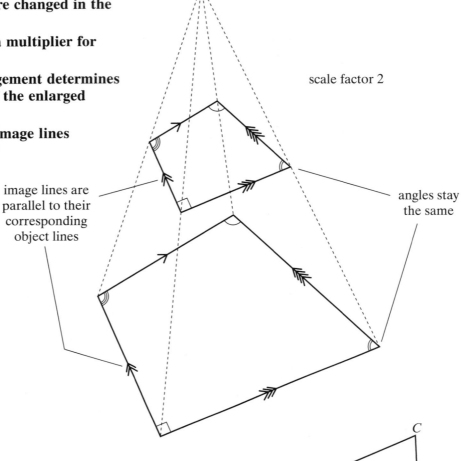

centre of enlargement

scale factor 2

angles stay the same

image lines are parallel to their corresponding object lines

Example 4

Enlarge triangle *ABC* by scale factor 2, using *B* as the centre of enlargement.

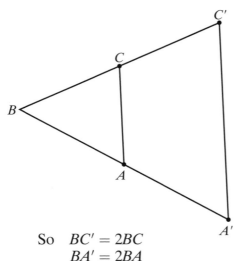

1. *B* is fixed as the centre of enlargement and does not move.
2. The scale factor is 2, so all the other points move 2 times as far away from *B*.

So $BC' = 2BC$
     $BA' = 2BA$

Example 5

Enlarge shape *KLMN* by scale factor $2\frac{1}{2}$, centre *O*.

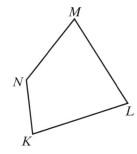

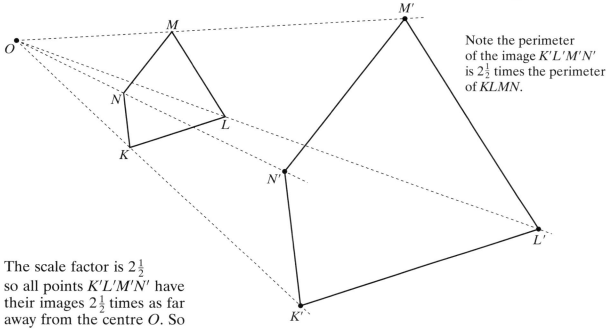

Note the perimeter of the image *K′L′M′N′* is $2\frac{1}{2}$ times the perimeter of *KLMN*.

The scale factor is $2\frac{1}{2}$ so all points *K′L′M′N′* have their images $2\frac{1}{2}$ times as far away from the centre *O*. So

$$K'O = 2\tfrac{1}{2} \times KO, \ L'O = 2\tfrac{1}{2} \times LO, \ M'O = 2\tfrac{1}{2} \times MO, \ N'O = 2\tfrac{1}{2} \times NO.$$

Example 6

On the grid enlarge shape *ABC* by scale factor 3, centre the origin:

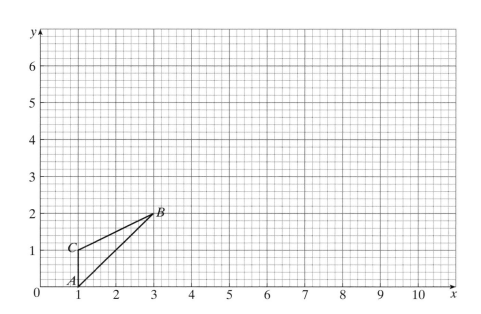

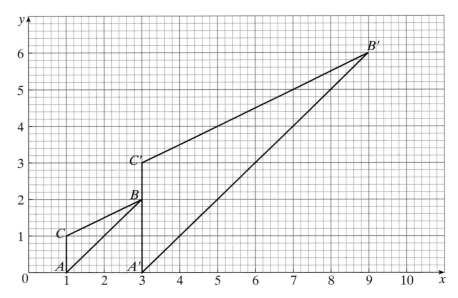

A is (1, 0) so A' is (3, 0)
B is (3, 2) so B' is (9, 6)
C is (1, 1) so C' is (3, 3)

Note:
angle A = angle A'
angle B = angle B'
angle C = angle C'

They are all 3 times bigger.

Example 7

Work out scale factor and centre of enlargement for these two
similar triangles:

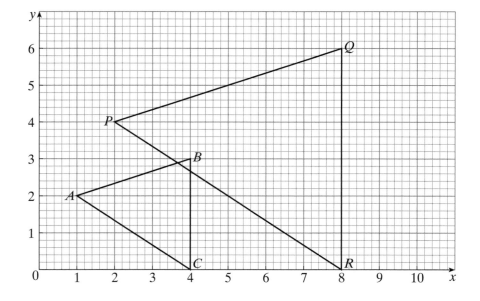

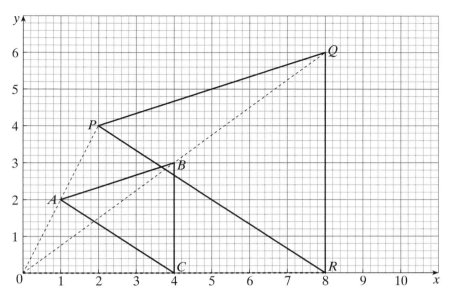

Join up corresponding vertices to find centre of enlargement, i.e. join AP, BQ and CR.

Here $2AB = PQ$

So scale factor of enlargement $= 2$.
Centre of enlargement is the origin $(0, 0)$.

Exercise 7B   Links (*22D*) **22D**

1   Each of the following shapes has a scale factor (SF) and two centres of enlargement. Copy each diagram and draw the two enlargements. Use squared paper.

(a)

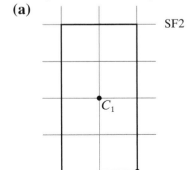

(b)

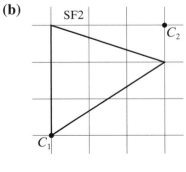

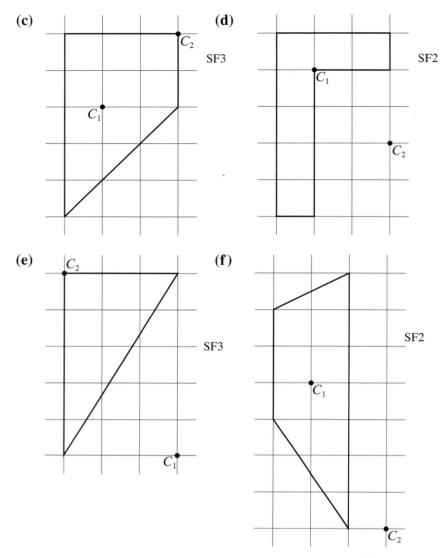

(c) SF3

(d) SF2

(e) SF3

(f) SF2

2 Copy *PQR* onto squared paper. Enlarge the shape by scale factor $2\frac{1}{2}$, centre the origin.

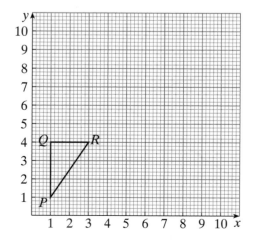

3   Work out the centre and scale factor of enlargement for each
pair of similar triangles:

(a)

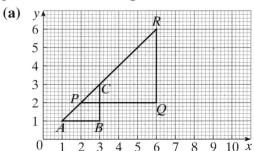

(b)

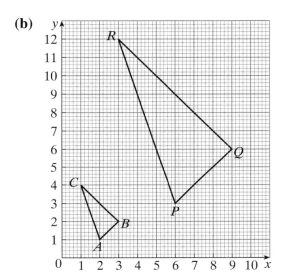

(c)

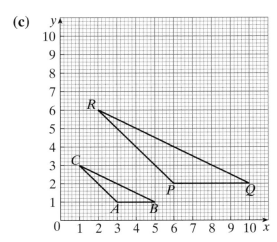

4   For question **3** give the pairs of corresponding angles for each
set of similar triangles.

5   For each part of question **3** write down the scale factor of
enlargement for the perimeter from *ABC* to *PQR*.

Summary of key points

- A translation moves every point on a shape the same distance in the same direction.

- To describe a translation fully you need to give the distance moved and the direction of the movement.

- In an enlargement all angles stay the same and lengths are changed in the same proportion.

- The scale factor is a multiplier for lengths.

- The centre of enlargement determines the final position of the enlarged figure.

- In an enlargement image lines are parallel to their corresponding object lines.

8 Statistics

8.1 Collecting data

- **Data collection sheets can be designed and used for continuous data.**

Teaching reference:
(*pp 111–115, sections 8.4, 8.5, 8.6*)

Example 1

Jaqui is working on a project where she needs to collect data about the heights of adults in her town.

(a) Design a suitable data capture sheet. Give reasons for your design.

As a result of an initial survey, Jaqui has the twenty results, all in cm, listed below:

178 156 201 180 167 176 173 143 173 175
203 196 182 178 163 171 163 155 183 172

(b) Record these results on your data capture sheet.

(a) Height is a continuous variable, so the sensible thing to do is to group the data. To group the data we need to decide on a class interval. We will use an interval of 5 cm.
The height of an adult is very unlikely to be below 130 cm and very unlikely to be above 210 cm. If we do get any exceptions to these heights we can record them separately.
We will also use tallies and frequencies.
So our data capture sheet is like this:

Note: there are no definite rules when choosing a class interval – it is a common-sense decision.

Height (h) in cm	Tally	Frequency
$130 \leqslant h < 135$		
$135 \leqslant h < 140$		
$140 \leqslant h < 145$		1
$145 \leqslant h < 150$		
$150 \leqslant h < 155$		
$155 \leqslant h < 160$	||	2
$160 \leqslant h < 165$	||	2
$165 \leqslant h < 170$	|	1
$170 \leqslant h < 175$	||||	4
$175 \leqslant h < 180$	||||	4
$180 \leqslant h < 185$	|||	3
$185 \leqslant h < 190$		
$190 \leqslant h < 195$		
$195 \leqslant h < 200$	|	1
$200 \leqslant h < 205$	||	2
$205 \leqslant h < 210$		

(b) The tallies and frequencies have been recorded on the sheet.

Exercise 8A   **Links (8D–8F) 8D–F**

1   Gary is going to work on a project looking at the mileage
    covered by some second-hand cars. No car will have
    completed more than 100 000 miles and no car will have
    completed less than 10 000 miles.
    (a) Design a suitable data capture sheet. Give reasons for
         your design.

    In a pre-sample of 40 cars, the mileages covered are as
    follows:

12 850	23 402	16 011	76 852	57 113	45 206	93 444	15 347
25 143	17 642	56 442	33 449	18 730	42 665	85 472	22 225
43 571	88 432	19 002	52 000	17 036	83 202	66 661	57 349
14 027	95 671	75 420	34 006	23 975	62 510	44 921	48 632
34 285	37 848	26 936	44 502	11 032	63 021	51 128	24 137

    (b) Record these values on your data capture sheet.

2   The maximum and minimum temperatures, in degrees Celsius,
    were recorded one day for 15 different holiday resorts. The
    results are given in the table below:

Max.	Min.	Max.	Min.	Max.	Min.
37.1	26.8	17.4	12.3	22.4	13.8
42.0	27.2	26.7	22.0	18.6	10.5
16.2	12.1	27.3	19.8	31.7	23.7
24.1	26.2	29.0	22.1	30.0	22.0
22.1	14.2	27.4	19.3	33.5	24.7

    (a) Design a data capture sheet on which these temperatures
         could be recorded. Give reasons for your design.
    (b) Complete your data capture sheet for the above
         temperatures.

3   Sumreen is doing a survey into the usual waking-up time of
    students in a school. She is particularly interested to see
    whether there is any difference between the waking times for
    boys and for girls.
    Design, giving your reasons, a suitable data capture sheet she
    could use for her survey.

4   James is working on a statistics project in which he wishes to
    find information about the distances students travel to school
    and their normal means of travelling to school.
    Design, giving your reasons, a suitable data capture sheet
    James could use for this project.

8.2 Scatter diagrams and stem and leaf diagrams

■ Scatter diagrams (or scatter graphs) can be used to indicate whether two sets of data are related.

■ The relationship between two sets of data is called *correlation*.

■ If the points on a scatter diagram are very nearly along a straight line there is high correlation between the variables.

■ Positive (or direct) correlation means that as one quantity increases then the other increases, or as one decreases the other also decreases.

■ Negative (or inverse) correlation means that as one quantity increases the other decreases.

■ If the points are scattered randomly about then there is no correlation.

■ No correlation does not necessarily mean no relationship, but merely no straight line type of relationship.

■ A line which is drawn to pass as close as possible to all the plotted points on a scatter diagram is called a *line of best fit*.

■ Data which follows a general pattern can still contain exceptions.

■ Data can be represented on a stem and leaf diagram, e.g. for ages 15, 16, 21:

Stem	Leaf
1	5, 6
2	1

Example 2

Gary works as a motor car dealer. At his showroom he has 10 cars for sale.
The price in £s and age in months of these cars are given in the table below:

Age (months)	32	11	46	60	73	8	22	26	34	48
Value (£)	5200	8500	4300	3600	2800	9995	7600	8200	6100	5000

(a) Represent this information on a scatter diagram.
(b) Comment on the correlation between the age and value of the cars.
(c) Draw the line of best fit and estimate the value of a car aged 40 months.

Gary has an eleventh car for sale.
This car is ten years old and has a value of £15 000.

(d) Plot this as an eleventh point on the scatter diagram and comment.

(e) Represent the ages of the first ten cars on a stem and leaf diagram.

(a) Plotting the points on a scatter diagram gives the following:

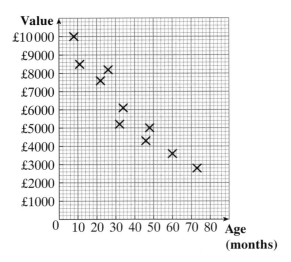

(b) The diagram shows that there is negative correlation between value and age.

(c)

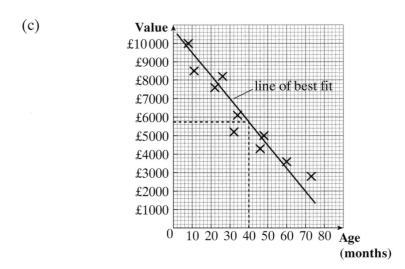

The line of best fit can be used to estimate the value of a car aged 40 months to be £5750.

(d) When plotted on the scatter diagram the 11th point is

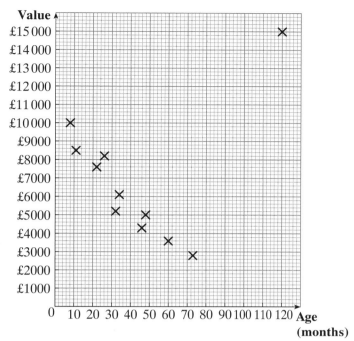

(10 years = 10 × 12 = 120 months)
This point is clearly an exception to the general rule that older cars are usually of lower value than newer cars.

(e) Using the tens unit of age as the stem, the stem and leaf diagram is

```
0    8
1    1
2    2, 6
3    2, 4
4    6, 8
5
6    0
7    3
```

Exercise 8B   **Links (25A) 25A**

1   Students' marks in a Mathematics examination and an English examination were as follows:

Mathematics	25	38	43	68	80	74	55	29	47	59	61
English	31	37	46	65	77	76	58	32	52	56	65

(a) Draw a scatter graph to represent this data.
(b) Comment on the relationship between the marks in the two subjects.
(c) Draw the line of best fit on your scatter diagram.

A student took the Mathematics examination and scored a mark of 50.
The same student was ill on the day of the English examination and did not take it.
(d) Use the line of best fit to estimate the mark this student would have been likely to gain in the English examination.
(e) Represent
    (i) the Mathematics marks
    (ii) the English marks
    on a stem and leaf diagram.

2 The table shows the hours of sunshine and the rainfall, in mm, in 10 towns during last summer:

Sunshine (hours)	650	455	560	430	620	400	640	375	520	620
Rainfall (mm)	10	20	15	29	24	28	14	30	25	20

The points for the first six results in the table have been plotted in a scatter diagram:

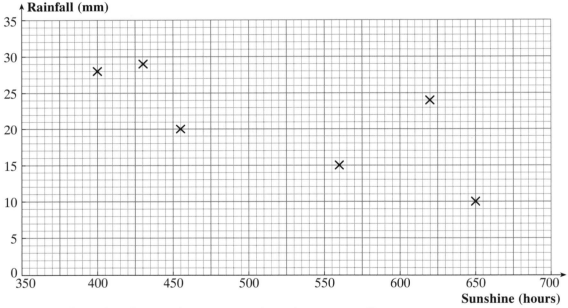

(a) Plot the other four points to complete the scatter diagram.
(b) Describe the correlation between the hours of sunshine and the rainfall.
(c) Draw a line of best fit on the scatter diagram.
(d) Represent the rainfall on a stem and leaf diagram.

3 There are 40 people on a coach.
Their weights, in kg, are given below:

43	32	64	85	71	38	57	52	63	51
91	77	62	72	55	54	62	67	80	49
51	63	70	63	44	48	64	57	62	72
54	57	42	55	61	90	66	61	50	69

Represent this information on a stem and leaf diagram.

8.3 Averages and range

Teaching reference: pp 308–316, sections 20.2, 20.3, 20.4, 20.5

- The mean of a set of data is the sum of the values divided by the number of values:

$$\text{mean} = \frac{\text{sum of the values}}{\text{number of values}}$$

- The median is the middle value when the data is arranged in order of size.
- The range of a set of data is the difference between the highest value and the lowest value:

    range = highest value − lowest value

- The mode of a set of data is the value which occurs most often or has the largest frequency.
- In grouped data the modal class is the group which has the greatest frequency.

Example 3

The weights, in kg, of ten people are as follows:

44   57   32   86   72   75   54   62   58   91

(a) Work out the mean weight.
(b) Find the median weight.
(c) Find the range of the weights.

(a) $\text{mean} = \dfrac{44 + 57 + 32 + 86 + 72 + 75 + 54 + 62 + 58 + 91}{10}$

$= \dfrac{631}{10} = 63.1 \, \text{kg}$

(b) Putting the values in order of size gives

32   44   54   57   58   62   72   75   86   91

There are two middle values, 58 and 62, so the median is $\dfrac{58 + 62}{2}$

$= \dfrac{120}{2} = 60 \, \text{kg}$

(c) Range = highest value − lowest value
$= 91 - 32 = 59 \, \text{kg}$

Example 4

The distribution of ages for the population of Madwell village is represented by the frequency table right:

Write down the modal class for these ages.

The modal class is the group (or class) with the largest frequency.
So the modal class is the age group 30 to 40.

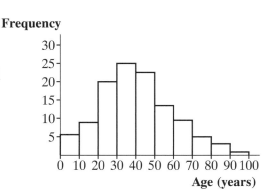

Example 5

The ages of 40 people are represented by the stem and leaf diagram below:

```
0    3, 7, 8
1    4, 5, 5, 6, 9
2    0, 1, 1, 3, 5, 5, 6, 8, 8
3    1, 1, 2, 2, 4, 5, 7, 7, 8, 8, 9
4    2, 3, 4, 7
5    0, 3, 6
6    1, 2, 4
7    1, 6
```

(a) Work out the modal class.
(b) Find the median age.
(c) Work out the range of the ages.
(d) Work out the mean age.

(a) The modal class is the group with the largest frequency.
     This means it is the group whose stem has the largest leaf.
     So the stem for the modal group is 3 – i.e. the ages in the thirties.
     The modal group is the age range

$$30 \leqslant \text{age} < 40$$

(b) The median age is the middle age when they are put in order of size.
     The stem and leaf diagram has already put the ages in order.
     The middle two values are both 32.

     So the median age is 32 years.

```
0    3, 7, 8
1    4, 5, 5, 6, 9
2    0, 1, 1, 3, 5, 5, 6, 8, 8
3    1, 1, (2, 2,) 4, 5, 7, 7, 8, 8, 9
4    2, 3, 4, 7
5    0, 3, 6
6    1, 2, 4
7    1, 6
```

(c) The range of the ages is

     largest age – smallest age

     so range $= 76 - 3 = 73$ years

(d) The mean age is $\dfrac{\text{sum of all ages}}{\text{number of ages}}$

$$
\begin{aligned}
\text{mean} = (\,&3 + 7 + 8 + 14 + 15 + 15 + 16 + 19 + 20 + 21 \\
&+ 21 + 23 + 25 + 25 + 26 + 28 + 28 + 31 + 31 \\
&+ 32 + 32 + 34 + 35 + 37 + 37 + 38 + 38 + 39 \\
&+ 42 + 43 + 44 + 47 + 50 + 53 + 56 + 61 + 62 \\
&+ 64 + 71 + 76) \div 40
\end{aligned}
$$

$$= \frac{1367}{40} = 34.175 \text{ years}$$

Exercise 8C   Links (*10B, 20C–D*) 10B, 20C–D

1   The heights, in cm, of 10 people are as follows:

162   174   155   132   201   188   175   168   146   187

   (a) Find the median height.
   (b) Work out the range of the heights.
   (c) Work out the mean height.

2   The mid-day temperatures, in °C, in 25 holiday resorts are shown below:

24, 23, 19, 28, 20, 31, 38, 32, 27, 29, 18, 26, 27
23, 30, 26, 29, 33, 28, 26, 26, 28, 21, 20, 25

   (a) Represent the temperatures in the table below:

Temperature (T)	Tally	Frequency
$15 \leqslant T < 20$		
$20 \leqslant T < 25$		
$25 \leqslant T < 30$		
$30 \leqslant T < 35$		
$35 \leqslant T < 40$		

   (b) Find the median temperature.
   (c) Find the modal class interval.
   (d) Work out the mean of the temperatures.

3   The mean of five numbers is 8.
   Four of the numbers are 7, 9, 10, 3.
   (a) Work out the fifth number.
   (b) Find the median of the five numbers.

4   The distribution of the weights of a group of people is shown in the grouped frequency diagram below:

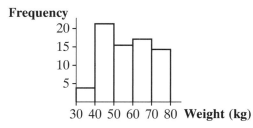

   Write down the modal class interval.

5   The speeds, in mph, of 30 cars on a motorway are recorded below:

44   42   60   55   81   72   75   48   56   68   59   75   72   69   80
50   52   66   71   68   73   56   62   58   63   60   64   37   88   73

   (a) Work out the mean speed of these cars.
   (b) Find the median speed.

(c) Work out the range of the speeds.

(d) Complete the frequency table:

Speed (s) mph	Tally	Frequency
$30 \leqslant s < 40$		
$40 \leqslant s < 50$		
$50 \leqslant s < 60$		
$60 \leqslant s < 70$		
$70 \leqslant s < 80$		
$80 \leqslant s < 90$		

(e) Write down the modal class interval for the speed.

6   There are 15 children in a choir.
Ten of the children are girls and five of the children are boys.

The mean age of the girls is 9.2 years.
The mean age of the boys is 7.4 years.

Work out the overall mean age of the 15 children.

7   The distribution of speeds, in kilometres per hour, of 60 cars
on a main road is represented by the frequency diagram
below:

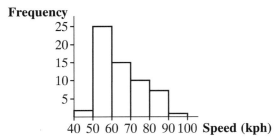

(a) In which class interval does the median speed lie?

(b) Write down the modal class interval.

8.4 Interpreting results

■ **Results can be related to initial questions.**

■ **Data may have patterns and exceptions.**

■ **Distributions can be compared from graphs, tables and diagrams.**

■ **Interpretations can be made from graphs, tables and diagrams.**

This section is a summary of the information covered in units 8, 10, 16, 20 and 25.

Example 6

Michelle did twelve homeworks in Science.
Her lowest mark was 4 and the range of her marks was 5.

She worked out her mean mark to be 9.4.
Explain why this must be an incorrect value for the mean mark.

The range = highest mark − lowest mark

So 5 = highest mark − 4
So the highest mark will be 5 + 4 = 9

Hence Michelle's marks varied from 4 to 9.
But the mean must be somewhere between the lowest and highest mark.
So the mean could not be 9.4.

Example 7

Tony's pulse rate was taken every 6 hours over 3 days last year.
The graph shows his pulse rate in beats per minute.

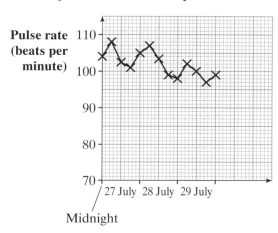

(a) Write down
    (i)   Tony's lowest pulse rate shown during these three days,
    (ii) when that pulse rate was recorded.
(b) Work out the difference between his highest and lowest pulse rate on 27th July.

(a) (i)   The lowest pulse rate was 97 beats per minute.
    (ii) It was recorded at 6 pm on 29th July.
(b) On 27th July the highest and lowest recorded pulse rates were 108 and 101 beats per minute. The difference between these values is

$$108 − 101 = 7 \text{ beats per minute}$$

Example 8

A group of boys and a group of girls took a spelling test.
The average mark for the boys was 8.
The average mark for the girls was 10.
Explain, using an example if you wish, why it is not possible to say that, in general terms, the girls did better in the test than the boys.

To make a full and accurate comparison we need a measure of average and a measure of spread, such as the range. Without both of these we cannot make a real comparison.

Consider, for instance, a case where there were 3 boys and 3 girls.
Imagine that the marks for the girls were 9, 10 and 11.
Imagine that the marks for the boys were 12, 12 and 0.

The mean for the girls would be $\dfrac{9 + 10 + 11}{3} = 10$

The mean for the boys would be $\dfrac{12 + 12 + 0}{3} = 8$

So the average (mean) for the girls is 10, which is greater than the average of 8 for the boys.

But it is not possible to say that the girls have, in general, done better than the boys when 2/3 of the boys scored a mark greater than the maximum mark for the girls.

Exercise 8D

1   The diagrams represent three scatter graphs:

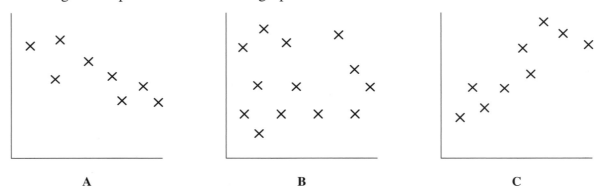

A   B   C

Use one of the words

Positive   Negative   None

to describe the correlation shown in each graph.

2   The scatter diagram shows information about the value of a house and the area of floor space for the house:

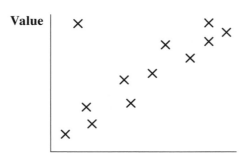

Comment on the implication for the relationship between value and area of floor space for these houses.

3 Georgina did 28 homeworks in Science last year.
Her highest mark was 18 and the range of her marks was 8.

When the Science teacher worked out Georgina's mean mark he told Georgina that it was 8.7.

Explain why the Science teacher's calculation for the mean mark must be incorrect.

4 The graphs below show information about the value of two cars over an eight-year period.
The engine sizes of the cars are 2000 cc and 1200 cc.

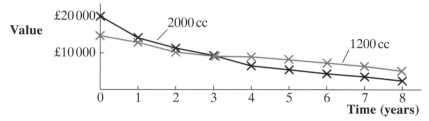

Make three comments about the relative prices of these two cars over the eight-year period.

5 The graphs below show information about the variation in average house prices in regions **A** and **B** over a ten-year period:

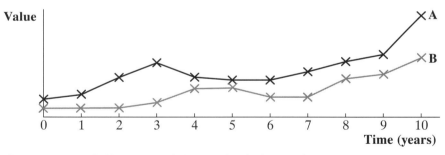

Comment as fully as possible on the information shown in the graphs.

Summary of key points

■ Data collection sheets can be designed and used for continuous data.

■ Scatter diagrams (or scatter graphs) can be used to indicate whether two sets of data are related.

■ The relationship between two sets of data is called *correlation*.

■ If the points on a scatter diagram are very nearly along a straight line there is high correlation between the variables.

■ Positive (or direct) correlation means that as one quantity increases then the other increases, or as one decreases the other also decreases.

■ Negative (or inverse) correlation means that as one quantity increases the other decreases.

■ If the points are scattered randomly about then there is no correlation.

■ No correlation does not necessarily mean no relationship, but merely no straight line type of relationship.

■ A line which is drawn to pass as close as possible to all the plotted points on a scatter diagram is called a *line of best fit*.

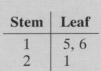

■ Data which follows a general pattern can still contain exceptions.

■ Data can be represented on a stem and leaf diagram.

■ The mean of a set of data is the sum of the values divided by the number of values:

$$\text{mean} = \frac{\text{sum of the values}}{\text{number of values}}$$

Stem	Leaf
1	5, 6
2	1

■ The median is the middle value when the data is arranged in order of size.

■ The range of a set of data is the difference between the highest value and the lowest value:

range = highest value − lowest value

■ The mode of a set of data is the value which occurs most often or has the largest frequency.

■ In grouped data, the modal class is the group which has the greatest frequency.

■ Results can be related to initial questions.

■ Data may have patterns and exceptions.

■ Distributions can be compared from graphs, tables and diagrams.

■ Interpretations can be made from graphs, tables and diagrams.

9 Probability

9.1 Theoretical probability

Teaching reference:
pp 355–360, sections 23.1,
23.2, 23.3, 23.4

■ Probabilities should be written as fractions, decimals or percentages.

■ An event (such as tossing a coin) can have different outcomes (such as landing heads or landing tails).

■ When one outcome prevents another outcome from happening, the two outcomes are *mutually exclusive*.

■ Outcomes which have the same chance of happening are equally likely.

■ The probability that something will happen is

$$\text{probability} = \frac{\text{number of successful outcomes}}{\text{total number of possible outcomes}}$$

assuming that the outcomes are all equally likely.

■ The probability of something happening is always greater than or equal to 0 (impossible) and less than or equal to 1 (certain). This can be written

$$0 \leqslant \text{probability} \leqslant 1$$

■ The probabilities of all the mutually exclusive outcomes add up to 1.

■ If the probability of something happening is p then the probability of it not happening is $1 - p$.

Example 1

Asif has a bag of 20 chocolates.
12 of the chocolates are plain, 5 are milk and 3 are white.
Asif selects a chocolate at random.
Work out the probability of the selected chocolate being
(a) milk
(b) not plain
(c) a sugared almond.

(a) There are 20 chocolates, of which 5 are milk.

$$\text{So probability of milk} = \frac{5}{20} \text{ (or } \tfrac{1}{4} \text{ if you wish to cancel the fraction to its lowest form)}$$

(b) Probability of plain $= \dfrac{12}{20}$

$$\text{so probability of not plain} = 1 - \frac{12}{20} = \frac{20}{20} - \frac{12}{20} = \frac{20 - 12}{20} = \frac{8}{20} \text{ (or } \tfrac{2}{5} \text{ or } 40\%)$$

(c) There are no sugared almonds in the bag, so selecting a sugared almond is impossible.

So probability of sugared almond $= 0$

Example 2

The probability of a new light bulb being faulty is 0.002.

Work out the probability of a new light bulb *not* being faulty.

Probability of not being faulty $= 1 -$ probability of being faulty
$$= 1 - 0.002$$
$$= 0.998$$

Example 3

The diagram represents a spinner in the shape of a pentagon.

The spinner is biased.

When it is spun once, the probability of it stopping on each of the sections A, B, C and D is shown in the table below:

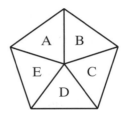

Section	A	B	C	D	E
Probability	0.23	0.18	0.16	0.22	

The spinner is to be spun once.

(a) Work out the probability of it stopping on section E (P(E)).
(b) Work out the probability of it *not* stopping on section A.

(a) The sum of the probabilities $= 1$

So $\quad 0.23 + 0.18 + 0.16 + 0.22 + P(E) = 1$
$$0.79 + P(E) = 1$$
$$P(E) = 1 - 0.79$$

So probability of stopping on E $= 0.21$

(b) Probability of not A $= 1 -$ probability of A
$$= 1 - 0.23$$
$$= 0.77$$

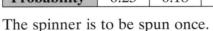

Exercise 9A   **Links (23A–D) 23A–D**

1   The probability of a newly laid egg being cracked is 0.03.
    Work out the probability of a newly laid egg *not* being cracked.

2   The probability of a train being late is 23%.
    Work out the probability of the train *not* being late.

3   Debbie has a bag which contains 10 equal-sized coloured counters. 6 of the counters are red, 3 are blue and 1 is white. She selects a counter at random from the bag.
    Work out the probability of the selected counter being

(a) blue   (b) not white
(c) either red or white   (d) green.

4 An ordinary cubical dice has one of the numbers 1, 2, 3, 4, 5 or 6 on each face.
The dice is biased.
Some of the probabilities of it landing with each face uppermost when it is rolled once are shown in the table below:

Face	1	2	3	4	5	6
Probability	0.20	0.11	0.17	0.19	0.21	

The dice is to be rolled once.
Work out the probability of it landing with 6 on the uppermost face.

5 A train can be either **early**, **late** or **on time**.
The probability of the train being early is 0.07.
The probability of the train being late is 0.24.
Work out the probability of the train being on time.

6 Imran has a box of 25 felt tip pens.
12 of the pens are red.
8 of the pens are blue.
The rest of the pens are black.
Imran chooses one pen at random from the box.
What is the probability that Imran will choose
(a) a red pen
(b) a black pen
(c) a pen that is not blue?

9.2 Estimated and experimental probability

■ The estimated, or experimental, probability of something occurring is

$$\text{estimated probability} = \frac{\text{number of successful trials}}{\text{total number of trials}}$$

and this is sometimes called the *relative frequency*.

■ The relative frequency, or estimated probability, becomes a better estimate as the total number of trials increases.

Example 4

The four candidates standing at the local election are named

Anderson, **Barnes**, **Clarke** and **Deyhna**

Shortly before the election, a market research company ask a random sample of 1000 voters the question

'For which candidate do you intend to vote in the forthcoming election?'

The responses to this question are listed below:

Name	Anderson	Barnes	Clarke	Deyhna
Number of voters	125	462	285	128

A voter is selected at random.
Using the information in the table, work out the best estimate for
(a) the probability of this voter voting for Clarke,
(b) the probability of this voter *not* voting for Barnes.

(a) The best estimate for

$$\text{probability (Clarke)} = \frac{\text{number saying they will vote for Clarke}}{\text{total number of people asked}}$$

$$= \frac{285}{1000}$$

$$= 0.285$$

(b) The best estimate for

$$\text{probability (not Barnes)} = 1 - \text{probability (Barnes)}$$

$$= 1 - \frac{462}{1000}$$

$$= 1 - 0.462$$

$$= 0.538$$

Example 5

The diagram represents a spinner.
It is thought that the spinner is biased.
Asif spins the spinner 100 times and records the letter it stops on.
His results are listed below:

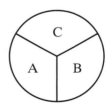

Letter	A	B	C
Frequency	28	30	42

Zoe then spins the spinner 100 times and records the letter it stops on.
Her results are listed below:

Letter	A	B	C
Frequency	26	36	38

(a) Explain why there is a difference between the two sets of results.
(b) Use the information to work out the *best* estimates for the
     probability of the spinner stopping on each of the three letters.
(c) Explain whether or not the spinner appears to be biased.

(a) Events such as spinning the spinner are governed by the laws of
     chance so the outcomes will be determined by the laws of
     probability. Therefore when an experiment – such as spinning the
     spinner – is repeated it is likely that the sets of outcomes – in terms
     of the number of times it stops on each face – will be different.

(b) The more times the spinner is spun, the better the estimates for the required probabilities. So the best we can do is to combine Asif's and Zoe's results to get

Letter	A	B	C
Frequency	$28 + 26 = 54$	$30 + 36 = 66$	$42 + 38 = 80$

We now have, as best estimates:

$$P(A) = \frac{54}{200} = 0.27 \qquad P(B) = \frac{66}{200} = 0.33 \qquad P(C) = \frac{80}{200} = 0.40$$

(c) If the spinner were unbiased then the probabilities of stopping on A, B and C would be

A	B	C
$\frac{1}{3} = 0.333$	$\frac{1}{3} = 0.333$	$\frac{1}{3} = 0.333$ (all recurring decimals)

We cannot be certain, but estimated probabilities of

A	B	C
0.27	0.33	0.40

based on 200 trials, suggest that the spinner is biased.

Exercise 9B   Links (*23E*) 23E

1   A market research company conduct a survey into the normal method of travelling to school used by students. They choose a randomly selected sample of 2000 students taken from all types of school across the country.
   The results of the survey are shown in the table below:

Method of travel	Walk	Car	Train	Cycle	Bus
Frequency	758	352	206	103	581

   (a) Work out the best estimates for the probability that a student chosen at random
       (i)   will normally travel to school by bus,
       (ii) will normally travel to school by car,
       (iii) will normally *not* walk to school.
   (b) Explain what the market research company will need to do to improve on these estimates.

2   The diagram represents a spinner.
   The spinner is thought to be biased.
   John spun the spinner 100 times and recorded the letter it stopped on each time.
   The results are as follows:

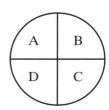

Section	A	B	C	D
Frequency	12	42	17	29

Mandy then spun the spinner 300 times, again recording the letter it stopped on each time. Her results are shown here:

Section	A	B	C	D
Frequency	41	129	58	72

(a) Explain why the frequencies in Mandy's table are not 3 times those in John's table despite the fact that she spun the spinner 3 times as many times as John did.

(b) Use the results to work out the best estimate for the probability of the spinner:

    (i)   stopping on the section marked C when it is spun once,

    (ii) not stopping on the section marked B when it is spun once.

(c) Explain whether or not there is evidence to suggest that the spinner might be biased.

3   1000 newly laid eggs to be delivered to a supermarket are checked. Of these eggs, 7 are found to be cracked.
Work out an estimate of the probability of a newly laid egg not being cracked.

4   The railway company check the arrivals of 200 trains. They find that of the 200 trains:

      12 arrive early, 142 arrive on time and the remainder arrive late.

Use this evidence to work out the best estimate of the probability of a randomly selected train arriving late.

5   George tosses a coin 100 times.
It lands Heads 57 times.
Jane tosses the same coin 100 times.
It lands Heads 45 times.

(a) Explain how these two results can differ.

(b) Explain whether or not there is sufficient evidence to suggest that the coin is biased.

6   The diagram represents a biased spinner:

When it is spun once, Jim estimates the probability of its landing on each section:

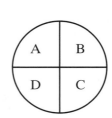

Section	A	B	C	D
Estimated probability	0.28	0.31	0.26	0.23

Explain why these estimates cannot all be correct.

Summary of key points

- Probabilities should be written as fractions, decimals or percentages.

- An event (such as tossing a coin) can have different outcomes (such as landing heads or landing tails).

- When one outcome prevents another outcome from happening, the two outcomes are *mutually exclusive*.

- Outcomes which have the same chance of happening are equally likely.

- The probability that something will happen is

$$\text{probability} = \frac{\text{number of successful outcomes}}{\text{total number of possible outcomes}}$$

  assuming that the outcomes are all equally likely.

- The probability of something happening is always greater than or equal to 0 (impossible) and less than or equal to 1 (certain). This can be written

$$0 \leqslant \text{probability} \leqslant 1$$

- The probabilities of all the mutually exclusive outcomes add up to 1.

- If the probability of something happening is p then the probability of it not happening is $1 - p$.

- The estimated, or experimental, probability of something occurring is

$$\text{estimated probability} = \frac{\text{number of successful trials}}{\text{total number of trials}}$$

  and this is sometimes called the *relative frequency*.

- The relative frequency, or estimated probability, becomes a better estimate as the total number of trials increases.

Examination style practice paper

Section 1 Answer ALL SEVEN questions.
       You must not use a calculator.

1   (a) Write $\frac{1}{4}$ as a percentage.   (1)
     (b) Write 90% as a fraction.   (1)
     (c) Write 0.35 as a percentage.   (1)

2

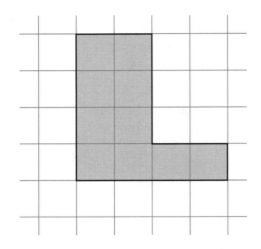

     (a) Find the perimeter, in centimetres, of the shaded
          shape.   (1)
     (b) Find the area of the shaded shape.   (2)

3   The rule for a sequence is **add 5**.
     The first three numbers in the sequence are 3, 8, 13.
     (a) Write down the next number in the sequence.   (1)
     (b) Find the 20th number in the sequence.   (2)

4   Find the value of:
     (a) 4^2
     (b) $\sqrt{64}$
     (c) the cube of 5.   (3)

5   There are 9 marbles in a bag. One of the marbles is red.
     3 of the marbles are blue and the rest of the marbles are green.
     Heather picks one marble at random from the bag.
     Write down the probability that she will pick:
     (a) a red marble
     (b) a green marble.   (2)

6   Alan's monthly pay is £800. He pays £280 of this in rent.
     Express £280 as a fraction of £800.
     Give your answer in its simplest form.   (2)

7

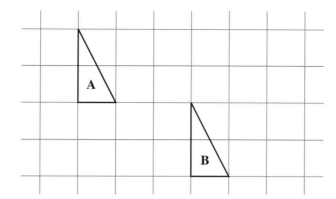

Describe fully the single transformation which maps triangle **A** onto triangle **B**. (3)

Section 2 Answer ALL SEVEN questions.
       You may use a calculator.

1 A carton of orange juice costs 63p and pears cost £1.18 per kg.
    Alison buys 4 cartons of orange juice and $1\frac{1}{2}$ kg of pears.
    Work out the total cost. (3)

2 John uses this rule to work out his take-home pay:

     Take-home pay =
     hours worked × hourly rate − deductions

    John worked 37 hours. His hourly rate was £5.37.
    His deductions were £59.42.
    Work out his take-home pay. (2)

3

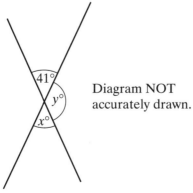

Diagram NOT accurately drawn.

  (a) Write down the size of the angle marked $x°$. (1)
  (b) Work out the size of the angle marked $y°$. (1)

4 (a) Solve $x - 5 = 8$. (1)

      $p = 3x - 4y$

  (b) Work out the value of p when $x = 5$ and $y = 2$. (2)

5

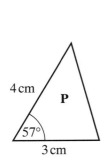
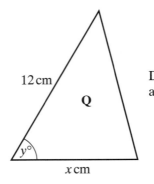

12 cm

Q

Diagram NOT
accurately drawn.

Triangle **Q** is an enlargement of triangle **P**.
(a)   Work out the scale factor of the enlargement.   (1)
(b)   Work out the value of x.   (1)
(c)   Write down the value of y.   (1)

6   When Amy comes home from a holiday in Belgium, she
      changes 25 euros back into pounds.
      The exchange rate is £1 = 1.62 euros.
      How much money should she get?
      Give your answer to the nearest penny.   (2)

7   Here are the heights, in centimetres, of 15 men:

          183   164   176   154   195
          157   186   162   179   181
          176   192   180   169   175

      Draw a stem and leaf diagram to show this information.   (4)

Answers

Exercise 1A

1 Next 4 numbers 16, 25, 36, 49
2 (a) 25   (b) 64   (c) 121
  (d) 9   (e) 225   (f) 441
  (g) 1600   (h) 10 000
3 Next 3 numbers 64, 125, 216
4 (a) 64   (b) 1000   (c) 512
  (d) 343   (e) 216   (f) 8000
5 (a) 6   (b) 9   (c) 10
  (d) 5   (e) 20   (f) 25
6 (a) 1, 4, 64, 81
  (b) 1, 8, 64, 125, 1000

Exercise 1B

1 (a) 32   (b) 256   (c) 1
  (d) 10 000   (e) 625   (f) 7776
2 (a) 2^4 (b) 4^5 (c) 1^6
  (d) 8^3 (e) 6^2 (f) 7^4
3

Power of 10	Index	Value	Value in words
10^3	3	1 000	A thousand
10^2	2	100	A hundred
10^6	6	1 000 000	A million
10^1	1	10	Ten
10^5	5	100 000	A hundred thousand

4 (a) 100   (b) 128   (c) 200
  (d) 6400   (e) 400   (f) 6000
  (g) 4   (h) 125   (i) 16

Exercise 1C

1 (a) 8   (b) 0.6   (c) 5
2 (a) 22.09   (b) 9.261
  (c) 1055.6001   (d) 2.985 984
  (e) 2.5   (f) 2.3
3 (a) 3.6   (b) 2.5
  (c) 17.986   (d) 26.042 (3 d.p.)
  (e) 8.875 (3 d.p.)
4 (a) 11.014 (3 d.p.)   (b) 2.2
  (c) 5.707 (3 d.p.)   (d) 0.970 (3 d.p.)
5 (a) 0.05   (b) 0.2
  (c) 12.5   (d) 3.333 (3 d.p.)

Exercise 1D

1 (a) [1] 2 3 [4] 5 6
    7 [8] [9] 10 11 12
    13 14 15 [16] 17 18
    19 20 21 22 23 24
    [25] 26 [27] 28 29 30
    31 32 33 34 35 [36]
  (b) 1
2 (a) 16   (b) 512   (c) 289
  (d) 9261   (e) 90   (f) 63
3 (a) 6^3 (b) 11^2 (c) 2^6
4 (a) 625   (b) 128
  (c) 1000   (d) 100 000
5 (a) 144   (b) 784
  (c) 400   (d) 30 000
6 (a) 3.351 (3 d.p.)   (b) 10.153 (3 d.p.)
  (c) 3.818 (3 d.p.)   (d) 1.429 (3 d.p.)

Exercise 2A

1 (a) $\frac{8}{15}$ (b) $\frac{7}{15}$
2 (a) $\frac{3}{8}$ (b) $\frac{1}{2}$ (c) $\frac{1}{8}$
3 (a) $\frac{1}{12}$ (b) $\frac{5}{36}$ (c) $\frac{1}{3}$ (d) $\frac{4}{9}$
4 $\frac{3}{5}$
5 (a) $\frac{3}{5}$ (b) $\frac{2}{5}$
6 $\frac{1}{5}$
7 $\frac{19}{20}$
8 (a) $\frac{12}{25}$ (b) $\frac{2}{5}$ (c) $\frac{3}{25}$

Exercise 2B

1 (a) $\frac{1}{5}$ (b) $\frac{1}{2}$ (c) $\frac{1}{4}$ (d) $\frac{3}{4}$
  (e) $\frac{8}{25}$ (f) $\frac{16}{25}$ (g) $\frac{3}{8}$ (h) $\frac{5}{8}$
2 (a) 0.3   (b) 0.7   (c) 0.45   (d) 0.85
  (e) 0.32   (f) 0.51   (g) 0.185   (h) 0.725
3 (a) 24%   (b) 30%   (c) 55%   (d) 60%
  (e) 37%   (f) $23\frac{1}{2}$%   (g) $17\frac{1}{2}$%   (h) $42\frac{1}{2}$%
4 (a) 90%   (b) 30%   (c) 60%   (d) 20%
  (e) $57\frac{1}{2}$%   (f) 16%   (g) 34%   (h) 37%
5 (a) Leo
  (b) $\frac{3}{4}$ is 75% which is less than 85%
6 (a) £555   (b) 30%

Exercise 2C

1 (a) £6   (b) £18
2 (a) £4   (b) £32
3 (a) £1.20   (b) £4
4 500 g flour, 250 g sugar, 125 g butter
5 (a) €404.15   (b) £194.85
6 (a) £250   (b) £187.50
7 4 days   8 5 days   9 6 hours

Exercise 2D

1 1500 m
2 (a) 150 miles   (b) 400 miles
3 (a) 5 h   (b) 8 h   (c) $3\frac{1}{2}$ h
4 (a) 4 s   (b) 7 s   (c) 50 s
5 250 ml   6 3.6 kg   7 9 m
8 4 mm   9 15 cm   10 36 l
11 $5\frac{1}{2}$ ft   12 90 kg   13 320 km
14 48 km per hour

Exercise 2E

1 (a) $\frac{1}{5}$ (b) $\frac{4}{5}$
2 (a) $\frac{12}{25}$ (b) $\frac{8}{25}$
3 (i) (a) $\frac{3}{10}$ (b) $\frac{9}{10}$ (c) $\frac{7}{20}$ (d) $\frac{17}{20}$
    (e) $\frac{9}{50}$ (f) $\frac{16}{25}$ (g) $\frac{7}{40}$ (h) $\frac{17}{40}$
  (ii) (a) 0.3   (b) 0.9   (c) 0.35   (d) 0.85
    (e) 0.18   (f) 0.64   (g) 0.175   (h) 0.425
4 (a) 50%   (b) 20%   (c) 80%   (d) 65%
  (e) 65%   (f) 56%   (g) $27\frac{1}{2}$%   (h) $27\frac{1}{2}$%
5 Lucy saved the most since $\frac{3}{4}$ = 75% is less than 76%
6 (a) £34.10   (b) €784.26
7 (a) 12 days   (b) $4\frac{1}{2}$ days
8 (a) (i) 280 km   (ii) 700 km
  (b) (i) 3 h   (ii) $5\frac{1}{2}$ h
9 6 cm   10 5 kg

Exercise 3A

1 $p = 3$ 2 $a = 5$ 3 $h = 9$
4 $e = 11$ 5 $n = 0$ 6 $g = 5$
7 $t = 9$ 8 $u = 8$ 9 $x = 14$
10 $v = 11$ 11 $d = 8$ 12 $c = 5$
13 $q = 7$ 14 $f = 7$ 15 $k = 0$
16 $y = 10$ 17 $r = 42$ 18 $g = 45$
19 $b = 48$ 20 $m = 0$

Exercise 3B

1 $y = 4$ 2 $a = 5$ 3 $h = 3$
4 $t = 3$ 5 $d = 2$ 6 $c = 1$
7 $u = 0$ 8 $v = 3\frac{1}{2}$ 9 $x = 1\frac{2}{3}$
10 $p = 1\frac{3}{4}$ 11 $q = 2\frac{3}{5}$ 12 $k = 2\frac{3}{8}$
13 $f = 1\frac{1}{2}$ 14 $n = 3\frac{2}{5}$ 15 $e = 2\frac{1}{2}$

Exercise 3C

1 $a = -4$ 2 $c = 5$ 3 $p = 6$
4 $b = 1$ 5 $q = 3$ 6 $x = 3$
7 $d = 5$ 8 $y = 3$ 9 $n = 7$
10 $k = 0$ 11 $u = 2\frac{1}{2}$ 12 $r = 2\frac{2}{5}$
13 $v = 4\frac{2}{3}$ 14 $t = \frac{4}{5}$ 15 $m = 2\frac{1}{2}$
16 $g = \frac{5}{6}$ 17 $b = \frac{1}{2}$ 18 $h = 1\frac{1}{3}$
19 $e = 4\frac{1}{2}$ 20 $f = \frac{2}{3}$

Exercise 3D

1 Perimeter = 35 cm
2 Wage = £185
3 Perimeter = 22 cm
4 Total pay = £235
5 Area = 40 cm^2
6 Take-home pay = £184
7 Average speed = 43 mph
8 Angle sum = 900°
9 Exterior angle = 45°
10 Area = 50 cm^2
  (to nearest whole number)

Exercise 3E

1 Length of each side = 7 cm
2 Number of hours worked = 33 hours
3 Width = 7 cm
4 Bonus = £50
5 Total distance travelled = 159 miles
6 Number of hours worked = 18 hours
7 Height = 3 cm
8 Time = $2\frac{1}{2}$ hours
9 Weight = 5 lbs
10 Vertical height = 4 cm

Exercise 3F

1 (a) $P = 18$ (b) $P = 42$
  (c) $P = 174$ (d) $P = 51.6$
2 (a) $A = 21$ (b) $A = 63$
  (c) $A = 22.2$ (d) $A = 37.8$
3 (a) $C = 6$ (b) $C = 16$
  (c) $C = 12$ (d) $C = 29$
  (all to nearest whole number)

4 (a) $E = 12$ (b) $E = 23$
5 (a) $y = 11$ (b) $y = 15$
   (c) $y = 23$ (d) $y = 18$
6 (a) $P = 16$ (b) $P = 31$
   (c) $P = 14$ (d) $P = 17.9$
7 (a) $F = 50$ (b) $F = 212$
   (c) $F = 86$ (d) $F = 32$
8 (a) $V = 40$ (b) $V = 120$
   (c) $V = 240$ (d) $V = 180$
9 (a) $v = 20$ (b) $v = 20$
   (c) $v = 20$ (d) $v = 59$
10 (a) $T = 90$ (b) $T = 135$
   (c) $T = 195$ (d) $T = 285$
11 (a) $S = 540$ (b) $S = 1080$
   (c) $S = 1440$ (d) $S = 1800$
12 (a) $t = 5$ (b) $t = 6$
   (c) $t = 5.8$ (d) $t = 6.4$

Exercise 3G

1 (a) $l = 4$ (b) $l = 9$
   (c) $l = 23$ (d) $l = 5.9$
2 (a) (i) $h = 9$ (ii) $h = 18$
   (b) (i) $b = 5$ (ii) $b = 15$
3 (a) (i) $F = 6$ (ii) $F = 14$
   (b) (i) $V = 7$ (ii) $V = 20$
4 (a) $x = 6$ (b) $x = 12$
   (c) $x = 3\frac{1}{2}$ (d) $x = 0$
5 (a) (i) $b = 3$ (ii) $b = 14$
   (b) (i) $a = 3$ (ii) $a = 5\frac{1}{2}$
6 (a) $x = 2$ (b) $x = 9$
   (c) $x = 20$ (d) $x = 2\frac{3}{4}$
7 (a) $h = 4$ (b) $w = 5$ (c) $l = 4$
8 (a) (i) $u = 5$ (ii) $u = 7$
   (b) $a = 6$ (c) $t = 4$
9 (a) $x = 20$ (b) $x = 85$
   (c) $x = 37$ (d) $x = 0$
10 (a) $d = 15$ (b) $d = 72$
   (c) $d = 45$ (d) $d = 56$

Exercise 3H

1 (a) 4, 7, 10 (b) 11, 6, 1
   (c) 12, 36, 108 (d) 12, 6, 3
   (e) 9, 17, 33 (f) 16, 12, 10
2 (a) Take 2 away (b) Add 6
   (c) Divide by 10 (d) Divide by 2
3 43 4 7
5 (a) Add 2 (b) 43

Exercise 3I

1 (a) (i) 10, 11, 12 (b) (i) 19
      (ii) 7, 14, 21   (ii) 70
      (iii) 3, 7, 11   (iii) 39
      (iv) 8, 10, 12   (iv) 26
      (v) 11, 17, 23   (v) 65
2 Twelfth term = 80
3 22nd term = 20
4 (a) Add 4 to the term number
   (b) Multiply the term number by 5
   (c) Multiply the term number by 8
   (d) Take 1 away from the term number
5 (a) Multiply the term number by 3 and
      add 5
   (b) Multiply the term number by 6 and
      subtract 5
   (c) Add 1 to the term number and
      multiply by 4
   (d) Subtract 1 from the term number
      and multiply by 8

Exercise 3J

1 (a) (i)

Shape number 5
   (ii) 11 matchsticks
   (b) (i) Shape number 6 has 13
        matchsticks
      (ii) Shape number 15 has 31
        matchsticks
2 (a)

Shape number 5
   (b)

Shape number	1	2	3	4	5	6
Number of matchsticks	4	7	10	13	16	19

   (c) Shape number 21 has 64 matchsticks
3 (a) (i)
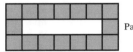
Pattern number 5
   (ii) 16 tiles
   (b) (i) Pattern number 6 has 18 tiles
      (ii) Pattern number 17 has 40 tiles
4 (a)

Pattern number 4
   (b)

Pattern number	1	2	3	4	5
Number of dots	5	8	11	14	17

   (c) Pattern number 25 has 77 dots
5 (a) (i)
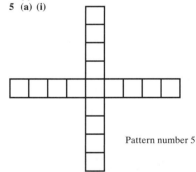
Pattern number 5
   (ii) 17 tiles
   (b) (i) Pattern number 6 has 21 tiles
      (ii) Pattern number 15 has 57 tiles

Exercise 3K

1 (a) $a = 5$ (b) $b = 4$
   (c) $c = 10$ (d) $d = 32$
2 (a) $a = 6$ (b) $b = 7$
   (c) $c = \frac{1}{2}$ (d) $d = 1\frac{2}{5}$
3 (a) $a = 3$ (b) $b = 5$
   (c) $c = \frac{2}{3}$ (d) $d = 3\frac{1}{2}$
4 (a) Total cost = £2000
   (b) Fixed costs = £700
   (c) Number of miles travelled =
      7200 miles

5 (a) $v = 15$ (b) $u = 28$
6 $A = 81$
7 (a) $P = 26$ (b) $P = 20.2$
8 (a) $C = 15$ (b) $C = 40$
   (c) $C = 0$ (d) $C = 100$
9 (a) $d = 31$ (b) $b = 28$
10 (a) (i)

Shape number 4
   (ii) 21 matchsticks
   (b) (i) Shape number 5 has 26
        matchsticks
      (ii) Shape number 17 has 86
        matchsticks

Exercise 4A

1 12 2 14 3 14
4 16 5 12 6 16
7 30 8 22 9 32
10 28 11 26

Exercise 4B

1 5 2 8 3 9
4 11 5 5 6 10
7 41 8 22 9 42
10 48 11 42 12 15
13 11 14 16

Exercise 4C

1 15 cm² 2 32 cm²
3 12.6 cm² 4 17.28 cm²
5 22.32 cm² 6 0.24 m²
7 0.81 m² 8 71.98 cm²
9 8 cm 10 10 cm
11 8 cm 12 12.2 cm
13 4.45 cm (3 s.f.) 14 5.25 cm
15 0.05 m

Exercise 4D

1 10.5 2 12 3 12
4 20 5 24 6 30
7 24 8 35 9 22
10 19.5 11 27 12 35
13 48 14 56 15 33

Exercise 4E

1

	Length	Width	Height	Surface area
(a)	4	7	2	100
(b)	16	8	3	400
(c)	21	4	5	418
(d)	16	3	2	172
(e)	10	5	3	190

Exercise 4F

1 (a) 60 (b) 30 (c) 32
2 (a) 192 cm³ (b) 81 cm³ (c) 168 cm³
3 (a) 33.852 cm³ (b) 92.872 cm³
   (c) 10.7 cm³

4

	Length	Width	Height	Volume
(a)	2 m	3 m	5 m	30 m³
(b)	2 m	4 m	5 m	40 m³
(c)	4 m	6 m	3 m	72 m³
(d)	5 m	5 m	8 m	200 m³
(e)	1.5 m	4 m	5 m	30 m³
(f)	8 m	3 m	2.5 m	60 m³
(g)	50 cm	0.2 cm	4 cm	40 cm³
(h)	0.4 cm	6 cm	0.5 cm	1.2 cm³

5 (a) 135   **(b)** 38   **(c)** 72

Exercise 4G

1 128 slabs   **2** 25.6 packs
3 £298.77   **4** 22.5 kg
5 36 drinks   **6** 360 bricks
7 500 boxes   **8** 100 boxes
9 48 packets

Exercise 5A

1 $a = 27°$ **2** $b = 104°$
3 $c = 58°$ **4** $d = 100°$
5 $e = 165°$ **6** $f = 53°$
7 $g = 117°$, $h = 84°$
8 $i = 144°$, $j = 36°$, $k = 144°$

Exercise 5B

1 $a = 88°$ **2** $b = 70°$
3 $c = 140°$ **4** $d = 140°$
5 $e = 238°$ **6** $f = 53°$
7 $g = 133°$
8 $h = 48°$, $i = 132°$, $j = 28°$
9 $k = 30°$, $l = 108°$, $m = 42°$
10 $n = 44°$, $p = 46°$

Exercise 5C

1 $a = 30°$ **2** $b = 27°$
3 $c = 37°$ **4** $d = 119°$
5 $e = 63°$, $f = 54°$ **6** $g = 34°$
7 $h = 45°$ **8** $i = 82°$
9 $j = 66°$, $k = 48°$ **10** $l = 54°$, $m = 63°$

Exercise 5D

1 $a = 118°$ **2** $b = 53°$
3 $c = 134°$ **4** $d = 70°$
5 $e = 65°$, $f = 50°$ **6** $g = 90°$, $h = 110°$
7 $i = 94°$ **8** $j = 120°$

Exercise 5E

1 $a = 45°$ **2** $b = 20°$
3 $c = 20°$ **4** $d = 50°$
5 $e = 18°$ **6** $f = 40°$
7 $\angle ADB = 30°$
8 (a) $\angle XBA = 10°$
   (b) $\angle CBE = 180° - 50° - 80° = 50°$
   so $\angle CBE = \angle BCE$ which means
   triangle CEB is isosceles

Exercise 6A

1 **A** and **C** are congruent
2 **A** and **C** are congruent
3 **A** and **C** are congruent
4 **B** and **D** are congruent
5 **A** and **C** are congruent
6 **F** and **G** are congruent,
   J and **L** are congruent

Exercise 6B

1 (a) 40°   **(b)** 140°
2 (a) 60°   **(b)** 120°
3 12 sides
4 (a) 18°   **(b)** 20 sides
5

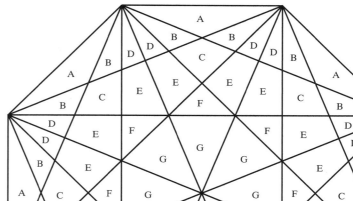

Shape A – 8 times
Shape B – 16 times
Shape C – 8 times
Shape D – 16 times
Shape E – 16 times
Shape F – 8 times
Shape G – 8 times

6 (a) $a = 150°$ **(b)** $b = 135°$
   (c) $c = 147°$ **(d)** $d = 260°$

1 (a)

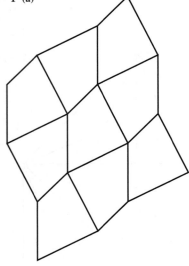

(b)

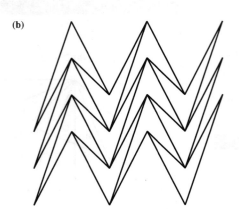

(c)

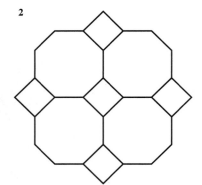

2

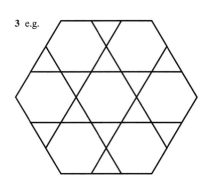

3 e.g.

Exercise 7A

1 **(a)**

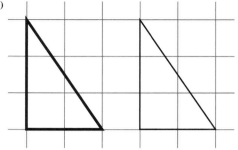

(b)

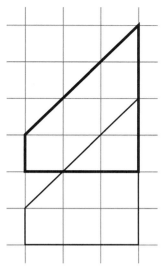

(c)

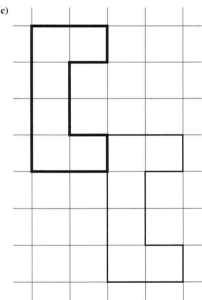

(d)

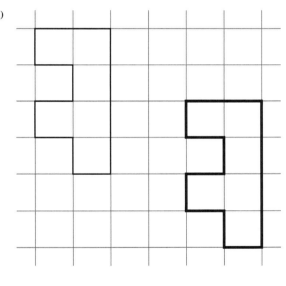

(e)

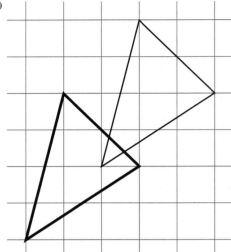

(f)

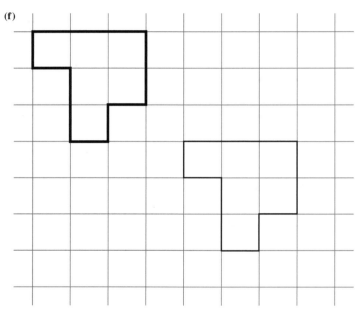

(g)

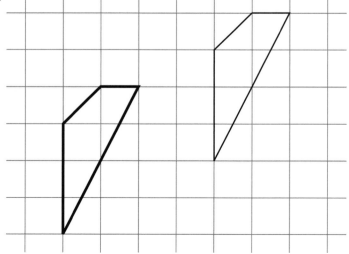

2 (i) **(a)** A (−4, 1) B (−1, 1) C (−1, 2) D (−4, 4)

(b)

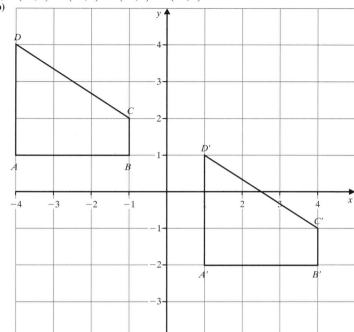

(ii) **(a)** A (1, −4) B (3, −4) C (3, −1) D (1, −2)

(b)

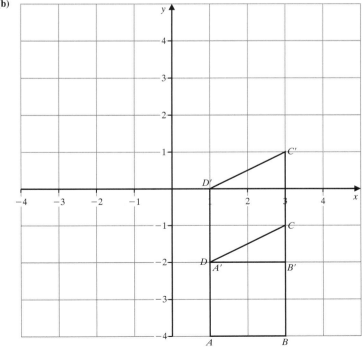

(iii) **(a)** $A\,(-1,1)$ $B\,(1,1)$ $C\,(1,4)$ $D\,(-2,3)$
(b)

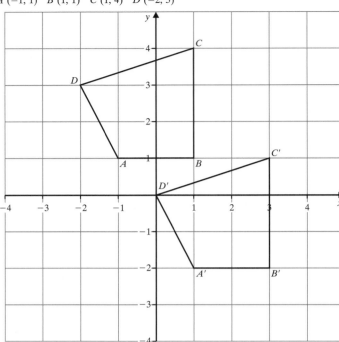

(iv) **(a)** $A\,(1,-1)$ $B\,(0,1)$ $C\,(1,3)$ $D\,(-1,0)$
(b)

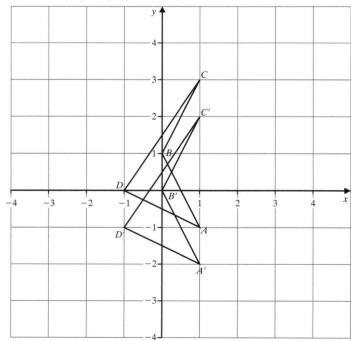

3 **(a)** 1 square right and 3 squares down
   (b) 1 square right and 5 squares up
   (c) 2 squares left and 3 squares up
   (d) 2 squares left and 5 squares down
   (e) 2 squares right and 4 squares up
   (f) 2 squares left and 5 squares up

Exercise 7B

1 (a)

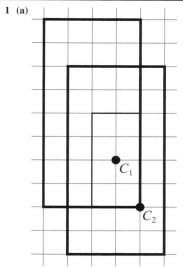

(b)

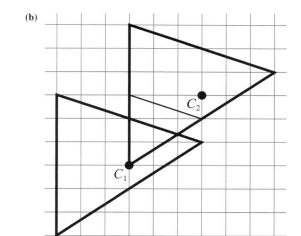

(c)

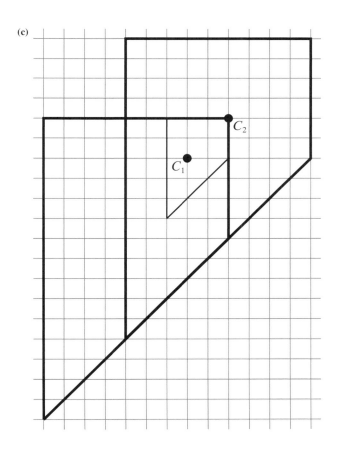

(d)

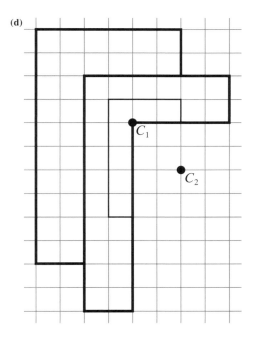

(e)

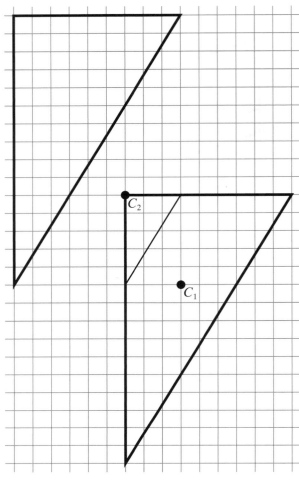

(f)

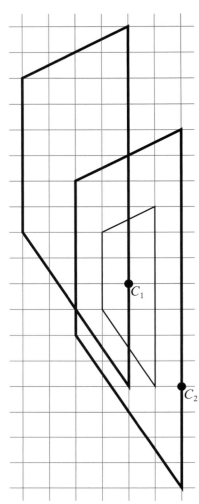

2

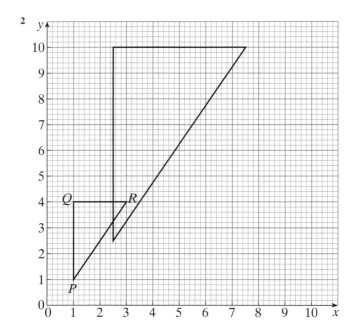

3 (a) Centre (0, 0), scale factor 2
   (b) Centre (0, 0), scale factor 3
   (c) Centre (0, 0), scale factor 2
4 Corresponding angle pairs:
   A and P, B and Q, C and R
5 (a) Scale factor 2
   (b) Scale factor 3
   (c) Scale factor 2

Exercise 8A

1 (a) Mileage is continuous so we should group the data. We will use a class interval of 5000 miles. We know there are no cars with mileage less than 10 000 or greater than 100 000, so our sheet will only be between these mileages. We use tallies and frequencies.

(b)

Mileage in thousands (m)	Tally	Frequency
$10 \leqslant m < 15$	|||	3
$15 \leqslant m < 20$	ⵌ		6
$20 \leqslant m < 25$	||||	4
$25 \leqslant m < 30$	||	2
$30 \leqslant m < 35$	|||	3
$35 \leqslant m < 40$			1
$40 \leqslant m < 45$	||||	4
$45 \leqslant m < 50$	||	2
$50 \leqslant m < 55$	||	2
$55 \leqslant m < 60$	|||	3
$60 \leqslant m < 65$	||	2
$65 \leqslant m < 70$			1
$70 \leqslant m < 75$		0
$75 \leqslant m < 80$	||	2
$80 \leqslant m < 85$			1
$85 \leqslant m < 90$	||	2
$90 \leqslant m < 95$			1
$95 \leqslant m < 100$			1

2 (a) We will record the min. and max. temperatures in separate tables. Since the data is continuous we will group the data. We will use a class interval of 5 °C. The max. temperature is not lower than 15 °C or higher than 45 °C, and the min. temperature is not lower than 10 °C or higher than 30 °C, so these are the ranges we will use. We use tallies and frequencies.

(b)

Max. temperature (T) in °C	Tally	Frequency
$15 \leqslant T < 20$	|||	3
$20 \leqslant T < 25$	|||	3
$25 \leqslant T < 30$	||||	4
$30 \leqslant T < 35$	|||	3
$35 \leqslant T < 40$			1
$40 \leqslant T < 45$			1

Min. temperature (t) in °C	Tally	Frequency
$10 \leqslant t < 15$	ⵌ	5
$15 \leqslant t < 20$	||	2
$20 \leqslant t < 25$	ⵌ	5
$25 \leqslant t < 30$	|||	3

3 She should have two separate tables for boys and girls. She will need to group the data, since times are continuous. A class interval of 15 min would be OK.

The students will wake up before school starts and probably not more than 3 h before school starts, so this would be a good choice for our range.
4 James should have a separate table for each means of travelling to school, e.g. walking, by bus, by car (with parents). Distance is continuous, so the data will need to be grouped. For walking, suggest a class interval of 0.5 miles, and the maximum distance is likely to be 3 miles ($\frac{3}{4}$ of an hour walk). For bus and car, suggest a class interval of 1 mile, with a maximum distance of 15 miles.

Exercise 8B

1 (a), (c)

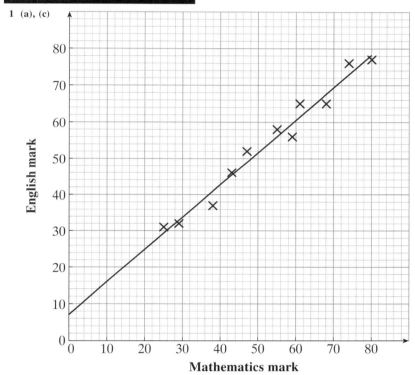

(b) There is a positive correlation between the marks scored in Mathematics and in English.
(d) 52 marks in English exam.
(e) Using 10s as the stem in both cases, we have
   (i) Mathematics

20	5, 9
30	8
40	3, 7
50	5, 9
60	1, 8
70	4
80	0

   (ii) English

30	1, 2, 7
40	6
50	2, 6, 8
60	5, 5
70	6, 7

2 (a), (c)

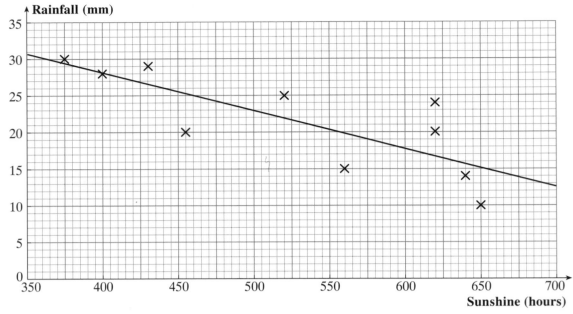

(b) There is a negative correlation between the hours of sunshine and the rainfall.

(d) Rainfall (using 10s as stem)

10	0, 4, 5
20	0, 0, 4, 5, 8, 9
30	0

3 Weights (using 10s as stem)

30	2, 8
40	2, 3, 4, 8, 9
50	0, 1, 1, 2, 4, 4, 5, 5, 7, 7, 7
60	1, 1, 2, 2, 2, 3, 3, 3, 4, 4, 6, 7, 9
70	0, 1, 2, 2, 7
80	0, 5
90	0, 1

Exercise 8C

1 (a) Median height = 171 cm
(b) Range = 69 cm
(c) Mean height = 168.8 cm

2 (a)

Temperature (T) in °C	Tally	Frequency
$15 \leqslant T < 20$	||	2
$20 \leqslant T < 25$	ЖН |	6
$25 \leqslant T < 30$	ЖН ЖН ||	12
$30 \leqslant T < 35$	||||	4
$35 \leqslant T < 40$	|	1

(b) Median temperature = 26°
(c) Modal class interval is $25 \leqslant T < 30$
(d) Mean temperature = 26.28°

3 (a) Fifth number = 11
(b) Median = 9

4 Modal class interval is weight 40 kg to 50 kg

5 (a) Mean speed = 63.2 mph (1 d.p.)
(b) Median speed = 63.5 mph
(c) Range = 51 mph

(d)

Speed (s) mph	Tally	Frequency
$30 \leqslant s < 40$	|	1
$40 \leqslant s < 50$	|||	3
$50 \leqslant s < 60$	ЖН ||	7
$60 \leqslant s < 70$	ЖН ||||	9
$70 \leqslant s < 80$	ЖН ||	7
$80 \leqslant s < 90$	|||	3

(e) Modal class interval is $60 \leqslant s < 70$
6 Overall mean = 8.6 years
7 (a) Speed 60 kph to 70 kph
(b) Speed 50 kph to 60 kph

Exercise 8D

1 A – Negative, B – None, C – Positive
2 The scatter diagram shows there is a positive correlation between value and area of floor space. There is one point on the scatter diagram which does not fit the correlation and is an exception (possibly due to the house being in a more expensive area than the others).
3 If Georgina's highest mark was 18 and the range was 8, her lowest mark must have been 10. As 8.7 is not between 10 and 18 it cannot be her mean mark.
4 During the first 3 years the 2000 cc car is worth more than the 1200 cc car. At about 3 years the cars have the same value, and for the final 5 years the 1200 cc car is worth more than the 2000 cc car.
5 Both regions have a general increase in the average house prices over the ten-year period.
The average house price in region **A** increased for the first 3 years to a peak at the 3 year point. Then the price decreased between years 3 and 6. Years 6 to 9 saw a steady increase in the price followed by a sharp increase in the final year. The average house price in region **B** stayed constant for the first 2 years followed by a slow increase in price for the next 2 years. The price levelled out between years 4 and 5, and then slightly decreased over the next 2 years. During the final 3 years the price increased fairly quickly.

All the time in the 10-year period the price in region **A** was greater than that in region **B**. The smallest difference in prices came in year 5.

Exercise 9A

1 0.97
2 77%
3 (a) $\frac{3}{10}$ **(b)** $\frac{9}{10}$ **(c)** $\frac{7}{10}$ **(d)** 0
4 0.12
5 0.69
6 (a) $\frac{12}{25}$ **(b)** $\frac{1}{5}$ **(c)** $\frac{17}{25}$

Exercise 9B

1 (a) (i) 0.2905 **(ii)** 0.176 **(iii)** 0.621
(b) The company will need to ask more students i.e. take a larger sample; this will make the estimates better.
2 (a) The outcome of the spinner is governed by the laws of chance, so it is likely that each time we spin the spinner 100 times we will get a different set of outcomes. So it is unlikely that Mandy will have 3 times the frequencies that John got.
(b) (i) 0.1875 **(ii)** 0.5725
(c) Our best estimates are P(A) = 0.1325
P(B) = 0.4275
P(C) = 0.1875
P(D) = 0.2525
If the spinner was unbiased the probabilities would each be 0.25, so the spinner appears to be biased.
3 0.993
4 0.23
5 (a) The outcome of a coin toss is governed by the laws of chance, so it is likely that each time we toss a coin 100 times we will get a different number of Heads.

(b) $57 + 45 = 102$

Best estimate is $P(H) = \frac{102}{200} = 0.51$

If the coin is unbiased this probability should be about 0.5, so our estimate does not give sufficient evidence to suggest the coin is biased.

6 $0.28 + 0.31 + 0.26 + 0.23 = 1.08$

But sum of probabilities $= 1$

So there must be an error.

Examination style practice paper

Section 1

1 (a) 25% (b) $\frac{9}{10}$ (c) 35%

2 (a) 16 cm (b) 10 cm^2

3 (a) 18 (b) 98

4 (a) 16 (b) 8 (c) 125

5 (a) $\frac{1}{9}$ (b) $\frac{5}{9}$

6 $\frac{7}{20}$

7 Translation 3 squares to the right and 2 squares down.

Section 2

1 £4.29 2 £139.27

3 (a) $x = 41$ (b) $y = 139$

4 (a) $x = 13$ (b) $p = 7$

5 (a) Scale factor 3 (b) $x = 9$

(c) $y = 57$

6 £15.43

7 We use 10s as the stem, so there are two digits in the stem.

Heights

15	4, 7
16	2, 4, 9
17	5, 6, 6, 9
18	0, 1, 3, 6
19	2, 5